Alive and Cooking:
An Easy Guide to Health
for You and Your Parents

To Mary,
It's great meeting you!
I send you wishes for
a life of joy, ease,
abundance & true health
Love,
Nancy

By

Maryann De Leo

and

Nancy Addison

Maryann De Leo
www.MaryannDeLeo.com

Nancy Alisa Gibbons Addison
www.OrganicHealthyLifestyle.com

Warning – Disclaimer
The purpose of this book is to educate and entertain. The authors and/or publisher do not guarantee that anyone following these techniques, suggestions, tips, ideas, or strategies will become successful. The authors and/or publisher shall have neither liability nor responsibility to anyone with respect to any loss or damage caused, or alleged to be caused, directly or indirectly by the information contained in this book.

Limits of Liability and Disclaimer of Warranty
The authors and publisher shall not be liable for your misuse of this material. This book is strictly for informational and educational purposes. *Maryann De Leo and Nancy Addison offer information and opinions, not as a substitute for professional medical prevention, diagnosis, or treatment. Please consult with your physician, pharmacist, or healthcare provider before taking any home remedies or supplements, or following any treatment suggested by Maryann, Nancy, or anyone referenced in books, articles, or other information in this book. Only your healthcare provider, personal physician, or pharmacist can provide you with advice on what is safe and effective for your unique needs or diagnose your particular medical history.*

"Love is never so great that it can't be expanded."

~ *Dominic Anthony De Leo*

Dedications

Maryann

I dedicate this book to my parents, Dorothy and Dominic De Leo, the lights of my life; to my two beautiful sisters, Diane and Dorothea; and to my three handsome brothers, Dominic, David, and Danny. I wouldn't have survived these past few years without their love and devotion to my mother and father, and their faithful support. They are all my heroes.

And to their families: my three beautiful sisters-in-law, Carolyn, Linda'Lee, and Joanna, and to all my nieces and nephews: Michael, Jeremy, Christopher, Ethan, Dean, Kristyn, Jenni, Lena, Dante, Lara, Ava, and Jesse.

Nancy

I dedicate this book to my parents, Junia and Patrick Gibbons, who, by their loving example, inspired me to raise healthy children; to my wonderful children, Amanda and Gibbons Addison, who have been my biggest fans and taste-testers all of their lives; to Gibbons's wife, Edy; and to my fabulous sisters and their families: Jane, her husband, David, their daughter, Claire, and her husband, Stefan, and their children, Audrey and Reid; Elizabeth, her husband, Layne, and their sons, Jack and his wife, Amber, and their children, Annie and William Ford, and Clayton and his wife, Lynsie; and Mary Katherine, her husband, Rusty, and their children, Katie, Becca, and Carter; and to my amazing, kind brother, Patrick, and his son, Ryan. They have all been my biggest cheerleaders and supporters, for which I am forever grateful.

Table of Contents

Introductions

Maryann

Inspiration has come from my father many times. My love for him and his love for me inspired me to live a full life, travel the world, keep an open mind, and think for myself, as he always did. This cookbook, too, was inspired by my father. I wrote it for him and to him, and I know he'd be happy to have me share what I learned with many others.

After living with severe emphysema for several years, he passed away from heart failure in the spring of 2010.

He lives with me in the interior of my life.

I was blessed with having a mother and a father who were geniuses, especially in their wisdom and commitment to feeding us pure food.

My dad had a garden 60 years ago. He never used chemicals on his vegetable garden or on the three fruit trees we had in the backyard. He was so proud of his garden. He grew the best, tastiest tomatoes, peppers, eggplant—everything from his garden was delicious.

He tended the garden as he tended us: with love. He was proud of his bounty. And I was proud to eat the tomatoes he planted and nurtured.

His garden was impeccable, as he was. With hard labor he weeded and turned the soil and fed his plants.

My mother's garden was on the inside—the kitchen, the hearth. She was brilliant and insightful, with an interest in nutrition long before it was trendy. She was the force inside our house; her stabilizing presence was security. The kitchen was her palette, her studio, her canvas.

A natural-born singer, she sang throughout her life, forgoing a career (we're all sure she would have been famous, including my father, who said, "If she'd listened to me, we'd all be rich!") to stay home and raise six children.

Instead she poured all her creative talent into us and my father, relegating her powerful, angelic voice to singing in the church choir, though she thoroughly enjoyed it. (She's been in the choir 50 years.) I took her voice for granted. Didn't everyone have a beautiful mother with an incredible voice, singing in perfect pitch?

My mother listened to radio shows on nutrition

60 years ago, making sure we ate foods that were healthy for us. My mother cooked for us every single day, making nutritious, delicious meals.

I have always been interested in nutrition, influenced, I'm sure, by my mother and father. But cooking and food became my obsessions during the past several years.

Since my father was diagnosed with emphysema, he had difficulty breathing while he was eating. We needed to give my dad food with high nutritional value, and that was easy to eat, to conserve his breathing. It's something I never thought about—that you breathe while you are eating; it was not until I saw my father struggle that it sunk in. We had to find food that packed the most nutritional power in each mouthful.

Doctors and nurses suggested commercial, high-protein drinks that tasted awful. I encouraged him to drink them because I was desperate to keep him from wasting away. But my friend Elizabeth reminded me that those drinks are full of chemicals. We ditched all the drinks (he must have known intuitively, because he never drank them) and instead gave my father nutritious yet easy-to-eat foods to accommodate his breathing challenges.

It was with love for my father that I became obsessed with cooking and recipes.

Cooking saved me. For the past few years when my dad was ill, there hadn't been much I could do for him.

He was quickly losing weight. In the winter of 2009 he weighed 80 pounds. I didn't agree with people who said to give him whatever he likes. How was that going to help my father get better? I wanted to give him foods that would support his health. I wanted him to get well. I'm not into torturing people with food they don't like, but I knew there were nutritious, delicious foods that my father would eat. I was determined to find those foods and cook them for him.

I'd watch cooking shows upstairs in my old childhood bedroom, memorize a recipe, and run downstairs to my mother's kitchen to try it out. My father was a good sport. He always tried my cooking, but he's not a faker. If he didn't like it, he didn't eat it.

The sweet potato–peanut butter soup was a no-go. "You didn't like it," I said.

"What was it?"

"Sweet potato–peanut butter soup."

"Peanut butter belongs on bread with jelly," he said.

But my variation on his mother's rice pudding is a dessert he would always eat. I substituted brown rice for white rice, and I used coconut milk instead of cow's milk. I did use organic sugar, but I cut down on the amount. I put in lots of golden raisins just like his mother did.

In a few months my father gained 10 pounds. I'm not taking credit for that; my mother took great, 24-hour loving care of my dad. She knows what he liked to eat, her cooking was his favorite, and she happily cooked for him for over 60 years. Despite what the doctors said, my father lived another year. His pulmonologist would visit, and look at my father and say, "Miracle man, that's what you are." My relationship with my father, in spite of his illness, deepened during that year, and those months became the most important time of my life.

My sisters and brothers and I all worked together to help care for my father, alongside the constant, patient guidance and care of my mother.

My sister Diane took a leave of absence from her job and stayed with my parents for months, giving my father nutritious foods (along with his daily dose of Vitamin B12) and helping my mother take care of all his needs, ready and willing to do everything and anything.

My brother Dominic lived with my parents while he was going to school. He got my father to eat quinoa and miso soup, drink protein shakes, and more. He took loving care of my father.

My sister Dorothea lives less than a mile away and was always available to help my father in any way she could. When she and her three children visited they always made my dad smile.

My brother David came several times a week on his way home from work, bringing my father tasty treats and coming every weekend to help any way he could. Often his wife, Linda'Lee, and their three beautiful children came with him.

My brother Danny lives outside of Boston. He and his wife, Joanna, have two young children, and still they made the long drive down to New York many times to spend time with my father and mother.

My father cheered up as soon as any one of my brothers or sisters walked in the door. All of my siblings contributed loving care for my father each time they came, bringing nutritious food and their love.

The food we all were cooking was having an effect: He was eating; he was coming back to life after being close to dying. When I was cooking for my father—chopping the vegetables, mixing the batter, standing over the stove stirring the brown rice coconut milk rice pudding—I felt alive again; I didn't feel helpless when I was cooking.

I invite you to find a way to enjoy time with your parents.

Cooking was my way.

Nancy and I were having lunch in New York after a trip she made to Greece to study Mediterranean cooking. She mentioned a cookbook she was doing for teenagers and vegetarian cooking. I said the book I wanted to write focused on nutrition and older people. We decided to write this book together.

I send this book out to share my love for my father and to help those who are still cooking for their parents and family.

Nancy

When I was 2, I became extremely ill from a penicillin overdose. The doctors told my parents I wouldn't survive the night. My father told me he prayed so hard that, when I lived, he said that he knew for certain that there really was a God.

I survived, but was left with acute anemia as a result. As I grew up, I craved any food that gave me energy. I started eating lots of sugary foods between my mother's meals. My doctor told my mother that if I wasn't careful, I would become diabetic. My mother started watching everything I ate. She made me high-protein chicken, egg, and salmon salads to take to school for lunch, and she made sure I ate well at breakfast and dinner. My mother carefully did everything the doctor directed her to do for me. I avoided becoming a diabetic. It was at this time that I began to understand that there was a connection among diet, nutrition, and health.

Since I was warned about eating too much sugar, I drank diet Dr. Pepper, thinking it was a better choice. I traded sugar for fake sugar and caffeine. Growing up in the 60s and 70s in Texas, my diet consisted of the "normal," standard food and drinks of the day. In Texas, that included fried foods, barbecue, trans fats, white refined foods, diet sodas, and packaged foods. I thought we were eating well at the time. We were living the American dream and enjoying the newest type of foods on the market.

I was a caffeine and sugar addict, because I was seeking energy.

Since then, I've found nourishing ways to conquer the sugar and caffeine addictions and be healthy.

After the birth of two babies 13 months apart,

I was over 50 pounds overweight, tired, and stressed. I was experiencing acid indigestion and headaches, and I developed carpal tunnel syndrome. My doctor told me I had hypoglycemia, and an x-ray showed that I had scoliosis.

When my father died of cancer, my son was 1 year old. That was a turning point for me, and I knew I wanted to see my grandchildren grown up. I really dug in and started learning as much as I could about nutrition, health, and holistic healing.

I began to study nutrition and health. I wanted to lose weight, get healthier, and raise my children without the health problems I had in my childhood. I had also become acutely aware of the unhealthy farming practices that were becoming mainstream, where animals were being given hormones to make them grow faster and fatter, as well as the addition of antibiotics being given to the animals to keep them alive, all while they were being raised in unhealthy environments. I was finding alternatives to buying this type of food. Since I was married to an environmental trial lawyer for over 23 years, I learned a great deal about the impact environmental toxins, air quality, plastics, dry cleaning solutions, water quality, etc. have on our lives and our health. As I changed my recipes and the quality of food that

I was using, my health problems disappeared: My acute anemia disappeared; I lost the weight I had gained (and I have stayed a healthy weight ever since); I don't even think of having headaches and indigestion any longer; my children's pediatrician told me that they were the healthiest children he had ever seen; and I feel really good. With a lot of various physical therapy, ballet, chiropractic adjustments, and deep tissue massage, I have also gotten the scoliosis to be something I don't even consider a problem any longer.

I have studied health and nutrition for over 27 years. I'm always adjusting what I eat. I know that the highest-quality food is always the best. I am still learning something new every day. What I do believe is that, when we give our body the right tools, it can do miraculous things in the area of health.

About the Authors

Maryann De Leo

Maryann is an Academy Award–winning filmmaker. Her latest film was nominated for a Golden Bear at the Berlinale in Berlin, Germany. Maryann is involved in many activities. She is a filmmaker, journalist, teacher at the School of Visual Arts, world traveler, student of handwriting and alternative medicine, and currently one of the UN representatives for the Women's International League for Peace and Freedom. She is also a home cook.

Her first book about Chernobyl was published in Japan in 2012.

She is working on a book about her father.

She can often be found attempting to persuade her family to try a new health food or a new alternative medicine modality.

Nancy Gibbons Addison

Nancy is the author of *How to Be a Healthy Vegetarian*. She is a member of the National Speakers

Association and a Certified Health Counselor by Columbia University and the Institute of Integrative Nutrition. She is a Board-certified health practitioner with the American Association of Drugless Practitioners. She studied detoxification with Natalia Rose, was certified by eCornell University and the T. Colin Campbell Foundation in plant-based nutrition, is certified for Basic Intensive in Health-Supportive Cooking at the Natural Gourmet Institute for Food and Health in New York City, and is a certified raw food chef, instructor, and teacher. Nancy studied Mediterranean cooking in Syros, Greece, with Australasian College of Health & Sciences. She also studied conscious organic farming at the Tree of Life and is a graduate of Hollins College (now University). Nancy is also an award-winning writer, artist, and photographer. She is certified in psychosomatic therapy with the Australasian Institute of Body-Mind Analysis and Psychosomatic Therapy. Nancy is a nutrition expert who counsels clients on nutrition, health, and food preparation one-on-one, in workshops, and at speaking engagements.

A Note from the Authors

We've collected these recipes and health tips for you and your parents.

Cooking for your parents is fun! Introducing new foods to them, as they did for you, is one way to treasure them.

The recipes in this book are a guide. Adjust and allow for your family's tastes and preferences. Be creative.

Foreword

By Leeann Lavin, author of The Hamptons *and* Long Island Homegrown Cookbook

Food is love.

Embraced by the earth, caressed by the sun, and kissed by the rain, nature respectfully shares her passions with us.

Food is art.

The art of food fuels our imagination and creativity. We create homes, traditions, culinary triumphs, and comfort through our interpretation of food's ingredients, preparation, and presentation. There is the saying "The eyes eat first," with the food beguiling our sense of sight—flirting with us before seducing our other senses of smell, touch, and, ultimately, taste. What other art form takes hold of us so? Food is powerful. But it is also markedly tender, nurturing, and sincere.

Food is a metaphor.

It is a tool, a constant garden where love is growing, waiting to be shared. To be served, given away with abandon.

Food is a journey.

It takes us to distant countries and faraway places. It takes us across time and generations. Food penetrates our hearts. And our memories. It is a passport to other cultures; a portal to our own unique past.

This book is transporting.

It reveals—or rips back the cover on the extraordinary connection to our families; our selves.

You could say the food stories and nutritious recipes are lessons.

Reading them, it's almost as if our lives depended on it.

It does.

The food chronicles here reveal an intimacy that can only be found in family heritage cuisines that are deeply and genuinely experienced: over generations, over the dinner table, over a lifetime of cheers, salutes, and amens. Our happiest, fondest memories are over celebrations of food and family. Big holidays and achievements. Romantic interludes. And quiet, tender, heartbreaking, private tributes.

My series of *Homegrown* books and writings explores the connection of master chefs to their inspired growers: the vegetable, duck, and honey farmers, oyster growers, and fishermen. My talented, sensitive artist cousin Maryann and her co-author, Nancy, have taken this concept of eating inspired local food to the next level. Naturally. While the concept of the book was sparked out of heartbreak and loss, let there be no doubt the book is one of enduring hope and love.

What could be more intimate and inspired than preparing nutritious, delicious food for family? Time spent talking and working in the kitchen. Meals shared. Traditions and heritage passed on in the glow of serving home-cooked meals with full plates and brimming glasses.

The recipes here are natural, healthy, organic, and prepared with sustainable ingredients, of course.

You will be inspired to cook them because each of the family recipes—our family—have been tested by time—and love. And in the end, they are truly the best ingredients.

Enjoy. Cheers to family—and food!

Part I
Food, Health, and Nutrition Information

(Listed in alphabetical order and not in order of importance.)

Beverages

The fluids we drink satisfy our thirst and maintain the necessary water content in our bodies. Hydrating fluids are the elixir of life.

Fruit juice is a delicious beverage. In its very nature it's already sweet, but fruit juice often has extra sugar added. Check the ingredients on labels. Also, fruit juices don't have fiber. Fiber helps slow the sugar going into the blood stream. Fruit juice lacks fiber and can go quickly into the blood stream and can make your blood sugar levels spike.

Fresh vegetable and fruit juices are hydrating. Juices lose a major portion of the nutrient value after about 20 minutes of being juiced; if you make fresh juices, drink them immediately.

Teas are a good choice for sipping throughout the day. Organic, non-caffeinated herb teas have health benefits.

Put fresh mint in tea or in pitchers of water. It infuses the water, giving it a refreshing flavor.

You can also add fresh fruits to water. Thoroughly wash the skins, then add slices to the water. Use lime, lemon, grapefruit, or any fruit you like.

Nut milk is delicious and a nice alternative to dairy milks. You can make almost any type of nut milk. There are so many to choose from. One milk I (Nancy) particularly like is cashew milk. The cashew is a softer nut, and because of this, it is easier to make into creamy milk. I use it in place of yogurt or sour cream. Cashews are lower in fat than the other nuts. They also have the same monounsaturated fat (heart healthy) as olive oil. Monounsaturated fat can help reduce high triglyceride levels in the blood. You can also put a handful of soft nuts like pine nuts in a blender with some water and blend to make an easy nut milk.

Liquid stevia comes in flavors and can be used with nut milks. There are lots of flavors, including vanilla, toffee, and lemon. Stevia will regulate the blood sugar and benefit the pancreas. It's a plant and is much sweeter than sugar, without calories.

Coconut water is a natural sports drink without all the added sugar and flavorings. It's unique, because the electrolytes of the coconut water are similar to human plasma. Doctors working in tropical climates during World War II and Vietnam used it for IV solutions.[1]

Beverages to Drink for Hydration and Health Benefits

Fresh juices (vegetable and fruit)

Purified water with added minerals

Purified water with added minerals and infused with mint, lemon, lime, grapefruit, or any other herb or fruit desired

Coconut water

Coconut milk

Herbal teas

Miso soup

Buying Bread, Crackers, and Flour

There are many choices when buying bread: whole wheat, gluten-free, whole grain, sprouted, and/or organic.

Labeling standards allow a product to have only a fraction of the claimed ingredients used and be labeled whole grain. A product can be mostly white refined flour and still be sold/labeled as whole grain or whole wheat. When buying grain products, check ingredients carefully and confirm that whole grain is listed as the first ingredient.

Whole grain or whole-grain wheat is better for you because most of the nutrients are in the germ of the grain. The fiber is the hull. When these are removed, the grain is left devoid of nutrients or fiber.

"Sprouted" is another term used in food products. When a grain is sprouted, it's more digestible.

When baking, many recipes call for white, refined flour.

White refined flour can harm the digestive system, because it is hard to digest. We recommend substituting whole-grain flour.

Many products today are made gluten-free. Gluten is a protein found in wheat, barley, and rye. Because of genetic modification, many gluten-containing grains today have up to 80 percent more gluten in them than they did 100 years ago. About 20 million Americans are gluten-sensitive. Symptoms range from digestive issues to depression. Many people feel better when they eat a gluten-free diet. Those who have been diagnosed with conditions such as autism or irritable bowel syndrome often find a reduction in symptoms when they consume healthier, gluten-free foods.

When I (Nancy) started making healthier food, I substituted various other flours for white flour. The non gluten flours such as quinoa, oat, and teff flour are delicious. Teff is a high protein grain from the Middle East. Quinoa is actually a seed that is a complete protein. Oat is a non-gluten flour, but it needs to be labeled gluten-free because it is frequently stored and transported in the same containers as wheat, and it will become contaminated with the gluten. Gluten-free flour will make bread a little less sticky than whole wheat. Sprouted whole-grain and gluten-free flours are easy recipe substitutions.

Store your flours in the refrigerator or the freezer to maintain freshness.

Choosing Meat and Dairy

Seafood: Buy wild Pacific fish. It's cleaner and less contaminated. Don't buy farm-raised fish. They're swimming in their own waste, and they are often given antibiotics to help them stay alive.

Beef: Buy organic, 100-percent grass-fed, free-range beef. Grass is the natural diet for cows. Grains and corn are unnatural for cows to eat and therefore change the molecular structure of beef. Buy organic, because you don't want antibiotics, hormones, pesticides, and fertilizers in your meat.

Poultry and eggs: Buy 100-percent certified organic, fresh, free-range (cage-free) fowl or eggs. Buy eggs from local farmers. Many eggs sold in the grocery store are labeled free-range or cage-free, yet the birds may be in closed-up rooms with no fresh air or sunlight. Do not buy Omega 3–enriched eggs, because that is not part of the natural diet of poultry. Ask local farmers what they "wash" their eggs with. Some farmers may only brush off debris, which is fine. If concerned about the shell's cleanliness, vinegar is the safest washing method for eggs. Fresh eggs will stay fresh for about seven days unrefrigerated. They will keep longer in a refrigerator. When cooking, room temperature eggs will work better in recipes. Take eggs out of the refrigerator about 30 minutes before you use them.

Dairy: Buy the freshest organic products you can find. There are some places where you can buy fresh, raw dairy products. It's almost an underground society. If you ask at the farmers market, you may find a place near you where you can purchase them. Make certain you are buying from a reputable farmer. Goat and sheep dairy is more easily digestible by most humans than cow dairy.

Cinnamon

"Cinnamon is emerging as a true wonder food in terms of health protection," says Ann Kulze, MD, a physician in Mount Pleasant, South Carolina, and author of *Dr. Ann's 10-Step Diet.*[2] Her research shows that cinnamon can help lower blood sugar, cholesterol, and triglyceride levels in people with Type 2 diabetes. She says that cinnamon contains antioxidants that create healthier arteries and reduce the risk of cardiovascular disease. Cinnamon can also benefit us with increased alertness and energized senses. Even a teaspoon a day helps tame blood sugar levels.

Ceylon cinnamon is the best cinnamon to use. A good way to add it to your diet is to sprinkle it on your morning toast, oatmeal, or other dishes.

Cleaning Fruits and Vegetables

Always clean all fruits and vegetables well. An inexpensive way to clean fruits and vegetables is to soak them in a mixture of unfiltered apple cider vinegar or food-grade hydrogen peroxide and water for about 15–20 minutes. Use 1 tablespoon apple cider vinegar or peroxide to 1 gallon water, or ¼ cup for a sinkful of water.

Electrolytes

Electrolytes are necessary for health. Unrefined sea salt has many different types of electrolytes. You can add electrolytes to the diet in various ways; using unrefined sea salt, eat water-rich fruits and water rich vegetables (like celery, cucumber, melons, etc.), or you can buy supplement packets in health food stores. One brand is Electrolyte Stamina Power Pak. The Electrolyte Stamina Power packets contain all of the major electrolytes and other vitamins and minerals. They don't have all the sugar and additives that other electrolyte drinks have. They are only 10 calories each; you just mix the powder into a glass of water.

Coconut water is another source of natural electrolytes. Coconut water is hydrating. Some coconut waters have a little fruit juice added to them, if you want a flavor. Check the sugar content. Some of them contain a lot of sugar. You can buy fresh young coconuts in many grocery stores; that is the best way to get fresh pure coconut water.

Vegetables and fruits that are heavy with natural water content, like cucumber, celery, and watermelon, are also rich with natural electrolytes.

Enzymes and Detox Cleansing

Enzymes foster health. Enzymes are important for healing the body, looking youthful, feeling healthier, and being more energized. Consuming foods rich with living enzymes will also make you feel more satisfied.

What are enzymes? Living food is whole food that hasn't been heated or processed higher than 105 to 118 degrees. Live enzymes that regenerate our cells and feed our body are bountiful in living food. As we age, we lose the ability to produce sufficient digestive enzymes.

Eating certain foods (such as meats), improperly chewing food, and chewing gum make our body utilize more of our digestive enzymes than necessary. These actions deplete the amount of enzymes for use in digestion. If the food we eat isn't broken down properly, our body won't completely absorb it. We absorb most of our nutrients in the intestinal tract through the intestinal wall. A clean intestinal wall will help the nutrients be absorbed. The integrity of the intestines is essential to our health and well-being.

Toxins and acid accumulate in our body over time through various actions like breathing polluted air, eating processed or fast foods, being exposed to carcinogens in various cleaning solutions, etc. Over time, they can build up in the body and create inflammation, as well as health and weight problems.

A detox cleanse helps flush out toxins deep in the body's cells and clean out the intestinal tract. A healthcare professional can help you find the right detox cleanse for you. We discourage a detox cleanse for anyone, especially the elderly, unless you are working with a reputable healthcare professional.

Anyone over the age of 40 should take a high-quality digestive enzyme supplement approximately five minutes before each meal. This will supplement the body's enzymes and aid the body's ability to break down the food being consumed.

Chewing our food is a function that serves to jump-start the digestive process while in the mouth and bring pleasure to consuming food. Chew food slowly. The better the food is chewed, the easier it will be for the body to digest it completely. Ideally food should be liquefied by the time it is swallowed. The more we chew our food, the slower we eat. It takes the brain about 10 to 15 minutes to become aware of the stomach being full. We tend to eat less, and digest our food more efficiently, by eating slower. In the American culture we are encouraged to drink liquids with our meals. Unfortunately, drinking liquid with meals dilutes the body's digestive enzymes and makes it harder for the body to digest the food.

Eat ample amounts of fresh, uncooked, organic fruits and vegetables. These whole foods provide nutrient-dense live enzymes that feed our body. Our health depends on the quality foods that are more alkalizing and grown fresh locally.

Processed foods and meats are very acidic. Disease thrives in an acidic environment. Our bodies need to maintain a certain pH balance in order to survive. If we eat too many acidic foods, our bodies will naturally attempt to adjust the pH balance. To adjust the pH balance and to become more alkaline, the body will pull calcium from the bones to neutralize or buffer the acid. Eating a diet high in fresh fruits and vegetables will contribute to a more alkaline-rich diet, which can help with the maintenance of the pH in the body.

Fat

"Good" fat is essential to our health and a healthful diet. Good fats support brain health, can prevent inflammation while working in unison with proteins and carbohydrates, and give us energy. In the last half century, there has been negative press about fat, and many food manufacturers removed fat from their food products. Since fat makes our food taste savory and satisfying, food manufacturers have added sugar, salt, and/or MSG to make non-fat and low-fat foods taste more satisfying. Read the ingredient list for clues about the health value of the item.

Trans fats are to be avoided completely. They are the hydrogenated fats that have chemically changed the fat into an unnatural condition. These are unhealthful even in small amounts.

Fats affect our health in various ways. Following are some properties of the most popular fats on the market and how they can affect health.

Popular oils used in our food preparation include olive oil, canola oil, coconut oil, and essential fatty acids. Nut, seed, and vegetable oils need to be kept cool (or refrigerated) and away from light. Oils stored improperly can become rancid. Oxidation rancidity is the degradation by oxygen of the fats. It primarily occurs with unsaturated fats. It's a major concern because it generates huge amounts of destructive free radicals. These can damage cells in every part of the body. Free radicals are a major contributor to over 60 different common health problems and the primary cause of aging.

Omega 3s are one type of fatty acids not made by our body, yet essential to our health; therefore they are called essential fatty acids. More than one type of essential fatty acid exists. Omega 3 is the one missing from most people's diets. They are anti-inflammatory and can be extremely helpful to anyone with an inflammatory problem.

Freshly ground flax seeds, flax seed oil, freshly ground hemp seeds, hemp oil, chia seeds, and fish oil are some main sources of Omega 3 fatty acid. Any of these can easily be added to foods. If you are using flax or hemp seeds, freshly grind them. If they are not freshly ground, the oils will dissipate and won't be as potent. Chia seeds do not have to be ground up for the body to utilize the oils in them. Fish oil may not be the best choice, because it can contain high amounts of mercury and low amounts of Omega 3. Read the label as to how much Omega 3 fatty acids it actually contains.

Canola is a genetically engineered plant developed in Canada from the rapeseed plant, a member of the mustard family. Rapeseed plant oil contains about 30 to 60 percent erucic acid, which is highly toxic. Canola oil has been developed to contain a range of 1.2 to .3 percent erucic acid. Many foods prepared at restaurants, in stores, and in bakeries use canola oil. There's controversy over canola oil and whether it is safe to use. It is highly processed. I (Nancy) avoid using this oil.

Olive oil can become rancid if heated or stored improperly. Oils have a smoke point. When the oil is heated and reaches its smoke point, the oil can become toxic. George Mateljan, a biologist, businessman, and nutritionist who is best known for his book *The World's Healthiest Foods,* told *Chicago Now* in an interview, "that olive oil should be heated below 250 degrees otherwise toxic fumes can be created from oil that is overheated. People are inhaling this smoke every day when they think it's being healthy, but in reality, the smoke from heated olive oil is full of toxins."[3]

When making the choice to prepare food with olive oil, choose organic, extra-virgin olive oil, from the first press of the olive. Be alert when buying olive oil meant to be heated. The labeling will signify if it is to be used for cooking.

Coconut oil is a saturated fat. It's a chemically stable fat and resistant to oxidation and rancidity. Coconut oil is highly effective as an antioxidant. Because of its chemical stability, use coconut oil for recipes that require heat. Always buy pure, extra-virgin, organic coconut oil, to be absolutely sure you are not getting a coconut oil that is a trans fat.

Coconut oil has medium chain triglycerides, which have been studied for preventing and treating Alzheimer's disease. The brain is nourished with good fats. Coconut oil is a good fat.

Coconut oil has ketones that help the brain recover from a loss of oxygen. Coconut oil is a saturated fat that raises cholesterol levels. There are two types of cholesterol: LDL, the "bad cholesterol," and HDL, the "good cholesterol." Pure extra-virgin coconut oil raises the HDL in the body. Dr. Beverly Teter is a lipid biochemist researcher at the University of Maryland. She says coconut oil is a natural antibiotic without any negative side effects. Because of that, the coconut oil will help defend the body against viruses, even going so far as to say it can help defend the body against HIV and herpes.

I (Nancy) have been putting coconut oil in my

smoothies for years now. I absolutely love it. I try to get at least a tablespoon of it in my diet every single day. I also combine it with flax seed oil, which gives me my daily Omega 3s, anti-inflammatory essential fatty acids. Pure, organic coconut oil and Omega 3 fatty acids are good fats. One question I am asked often is: How do I know the coconut oil or other oils I am buying are not trans fats? You do this by reading the labels and purchasing pure, organic oils and fats.

Dr. Newport, who cured her husband of Alzheimer's disease, also put Omega 3 fatty acids in her husband's diet, along with the coconut oil.[4] She concluded it cured him of the Alzheimer's disease. It has possibilities of assisting the treatment of Parkinson's disease, Huntington 's disease, multiple sclerosis, ALS, and brittle types of diabetes.

The foods you prepare and eat will taste more satisfying when you have a healthy fat added to them. Choose fresh, organic, whole food, cold-pressed, non-processed fats, and enjoy your food.

Fruits and Their Health Benefits

Fresh fruit is nutrient-dense, and full of natural electrolytes and live enzymes. Eat fresh fruit first thing in the morning on an empty stomach. Fruits are a pure food. When eaten raw on an empty stomach, the body digests and utilizes the fruit more easily and more completely than it does most other foods.

Apples. Apples are fiber-rich, and can aid in digestion. Apples can help with stimulating the appetite, and the pectin in them helps supports the immune system. Remove apple seeds and don't juice them, because they contain cyanide compounds.

Apricots. Apricots are commonly used to treat anemia.[5] Apricots are rich in Vitamin A and a good source of potassium. Buy unsweetened and unsulphured dried fruit.

Bananas. Bananas are rich in potassium, Vitamin C, and manganese, and are a very good source of Vitamin B6. Bananas can make smoothies creamy and sweet.

Berries. Berries are a great antioxidant food.

Blueberries, strawberries, raspberries, black-berries, mulberries, and cranberries are all rich in antioxidants; the antioxidants are in the color! Do not wash berries until you are ready to use them, as they are fragile in nature, and that will break them down and make them spoil quicker.

Blueberries. Blueberries are rich with Vitamin C, Vitamin B complex, Vitamin E, Vitamin A, copper, selenium, zinc, and iron. I (Maryann) like to use Wyman's of Maine fresh frozen wild blueberries in my smoothies.

Cantaloupes. Cantaloupes are a rich source of beta carotene. They also are rich in Vitamins A and C, and potassium, with some niacin and iron. Wash cantaloupes before cutting, as they have a tendency to mildew in the field, and the knife will drag the germs down into the fruit when it's cut.

Cherries. Cherries are a rich antioxidant food. They are used for treating anemia, are good for circulation, and can help with numbness in the limbs. Drinking tart cherry juice late at night is supposed to be a natural aid for better sleep. One particular tart cherry, the Montmorency, contains a good quantity of melatonin. Melatonin is a hormone that the pineal gland produces. We produce less of it as we age, which can result in poor sleeping or insomnia. Store cherries in the refrigerator and use them within a few days. Wash cherries as you use them.

Dates. Dates are a good sweetener to use in smoothies. They are full of fiber, vitamins, and nutrients, including B complex vitamins. Dates also help make hemoglobin, the red and white blood cells, and help with relieving constipation. Dates have properties that cleanse the intestines. Medjool dates, known as the king of dates and the finest type to buy, are grown in Egypt and California. Date sugar is made of dried dates that are ground finely. This is a healthier version of sugar. Dates are not recommended for people with diabetes, obesity, yeast infections, and respiratory infections.

Figs. Figs are sweet and nutrient-dense. Figs are a great energy food, and can help relieve fatigue and boost memory power. Figs are high in calcium, potassium, and fiber. Figs were one of Cleopatra's favorite foods. They are wonderful for hair, skin, nails, and digestion, and are detoxifying. Figs can act as a laxative and are good for bowel-related problems. Drinking fig juice can help soothe irritated bronchial passages.

Goji berries. Goji berries are super-antioxidant

berries. They can be added to a smoothie, but they will blend better if they are soaked for a few hours in order to soften them, because they are usually stored dried. Gogi berries are rich with Vitamin A. Vitamin A is known for helping boost the immune system and is good for eyesight. There are some "possible herb-drug interactions with goji berries."[6] If you take warfarin (a blood thinner), you may want to avoid goji berries. Goji berries may also interact with diabetes and blood pressure drugs. Also, if you have pollen allergies, you may want to stay away from this fruit. However, when eaten in moderation, goji berries appear to be safe. Ask your doctor if you have any questions.

Grapes. Grapes contain many vitamins (A, C, E, and K), phosphorous, potassium, and magnesium. The Vitamin C really boosts our defenses against colds or illness. The magnesium can help with muscle contractions.

Grapefruits.[7] Choose grapefruits that are the heaviest. They will have more juice in them. Grapefruits have a high water content and fat-burning enzymes. They are rich in Vitamin C and lycopene. Check to make sure that eating grapefruit doesn't interfere with any medications that are being consumed.

Lemons/Limes. Choose lemons and limes that are the heaviest in weight. They have more juice. They are high in Vitamin C, and they have anti-microbial and germ-killing properties. Because of these properties, these fruits can "destroy putrefactive bacteria in both the intestines and the mouth, used to purify the breath," and this ability makes them "useful during dysentery, colds, flus, hacking coughs, and parasite infestation."[8] An easy way to cleanse the organs is to juice half a lemon or lime, mix it with some warm water, and drink it first thing in the morning on an empty stomach. Limes tend to have fewer pesticides used on them, if you can't find organic lemons or limes. Citric acid can thin the blood, so anyone with "weak blood signs such as pale complexion and tongue, insomnia, irritability, and thinness" should use caution when eating lemons and limes.[9] Store lemons and limes in the refrigerator.

Oranges. Choose oranges that are the heaviest, as they will have more juice in them. Eating oranges can provide fiber. "Oranges have been valuable to inflammatory diseases such as arthritis; they also help lower high fever; their vitamin C/bioflavonoid content benefits those with weak gums and teeth."[10] Oranges are high in Vitamin A, Vitamin C, and potassium. Store oranges in the refrigerator.

Papayas. Papayas help the digestive system. They are rich in digestive enzymes that help digest protein. The black seeds are edible and a high protein source. Papayas are rich in Vitamin A, Vitamin C, and potassium. "Papaya also contain carpaine, a compound providing anti-tumor activity."[11]

Peaches. Peaches are hydrating. They are also helpful with bowel movements and the skin/complexion. They are rich in Vitamin A, Vitamin C, potassium, niacin, iron, and fiber. Store peaches in the refrigerator for longer freshness.

Pears. Pears are a good source of Vitamin C and copper. Copper helps protect the body from free radicals. Pears are helpful for the lungs, cardiovascular system, and colon. Pears can help with excess mucus and quenching thirst. This fruit is highly perishable, and should be handled gently and stored in the refrigerator.

Persimmons. Persimmons are rich in fiber, and have a high Vitamin A and Vitamin C content. Persimmons can help tone the spleen and/or pancreas, can aid the digestive tract, and are a nice astringent for the body. Persimmons can help with excess mucus or phlegm. Persimmons are usually available from September to December. Pick ones with a round, plump, glossy look and a deep color. Eat them quickly, or they will get mushy. Wash them, remove the stem, remove the seeds, and cut them up for salads or salsas.

Pineapples. Pineapples have digestive enzymes and help with digestion, constipation, and diarrhea. Don't eat them if you have a peptic ulcer.[12] The digestive enzymes made from pineapples can corrode and irritate the areas in the stomach that have been injured by the ulcer. Pineapples are a good source of Vitamin C, iron, and potassium. Choose pineapples with deep, rich green leaves. They should have a distinctly sweet pineapple aroma. Store them in the refrigerator.

Plums. Plums support the liver.[13] They are rich in Vitamin A, potassium, iron, pectin, copper, zinc, magnesium, boron, and fiber. The pectin can help with lowering cholesterol. Plums can aid with dehydration as well. Dried plums (prunes) are used for more than just their laxative benefits. Dark dried plums rank very high in the antioxidant levels.

Pomegranates. Pomegranates are rich in anti-oxidants. Pomegranates have been researched widely for their beneficial effects on cancer, tumors, and overall health. "More recent research has found that 8 ounces of pomegranate juice daily for three months improved the amount of oxygen getting to the heart muscle of patients with coronary heart disease."[14] Other researchers report that long-term consumption of pomegranate juice may help combat erectile dysfunction.[15]

Raspberries. Do not wash the berries until you use them; they are fragile and crush easily. Raspberries are rich in niacin, iron, potassium, Vitamin A, and Vitamin C. Store them in the refrigerator.

Strawberries. Strawberries are rich in Vitamin C, potassium, and iron. If strawberries are eaten before meals, they can aid in the digestive process. Buy organic strawberries; conventional strawberries are heavily sprayed with chemicals.

Watermelon. The entire fruit can be eaten. Watermelon skin is rich with chlorophyll. Don't drink too much of the juiced watermelon rind at a time, because it is a diuretic. Watermelon has high levels of nutrients, making it the perfect healthy treat. Watermelons are packed with Vitamin C, Vitamin A, Vitamin B6, Vitamin B1, potassium, and magnesium. In addition, medical studies have shown that watermelon can help with inflammation conditions like asthma, atherosclerosis, diabetes, colon cancer, and arthritis. It is also high in the antioxidant lycopene, which has cancer-preventing properties and helps oxidize cholesterol. Author Paul Pitchford, in *Healing with Whole Foods,* cautions that watermelon are "not to be used by those with weak digestion, anemia, or excessive or uncontrolled urination."[16]

The Dirty Dozen

The "Dirty Dozen" was established by the Environmental Working Group (EWG), a non-profit organization whose mission is to protect public health and the environment. The Dirty Dozen is a list of the 12 fruits and vegetables with the highest pesticide residue:

Apples
Celery
Sweet bell peppers
Peaches
Strawberries
Nectarines (imported)
Grapes
Spinach
Lettuce
Cucumbers
Blueberries (domestic)
Potatoes

In 2012, the EWG created a "Dirty Dozen Plus" category, which includes green beans, kale, and collard greens.

Magnesium

Magnesium is vital to health. If we aren't eating enough magnesium-rich foods, we can experience low energy, headaches, anxiousness, fatigue, weakness, PMS and hormonal imbalance, an inability to sleep, weakening bones, muscle tension, spasms and cramps, abnormal heart rhythms, nervousness, and irritability. According to new studies, women who had lower dietary magnesium consumption had a significantly higher risk of sudden cardiac death.[17] Lack of magnesium-rich foods, emotional stress, some drugs (diuretics, antibiotics, birth control pills, insulin, and cortisone), heavy exercise, diabetes, gastrointestinal disorders, and excessive calcium in the diet can lead to a severe deficiency in magnesium.

Some good food sources of magnesium are: green leafy vegetables (for example, spinach and Swiss chard), some beans, nuts, seeds (almonds, pumpkin seeds, sunflower seeds, sesame seeds), and avocados.

One of my (Nancy's) favorite supplements is a magnesium-rich powder by Natural Vitality called

"Natural Calm." It comes in a raspberry, lemon, and other flavors. It is highly absorbable, unlike some other magnesium supplements. You just take 3 teaspoons a day mixed in a glass of water.

Probiotics

Probiotics are good bacteria that support our immune system and keep the bad bacteria under control. When we take antibiotics, both good and bad bacteria are killed. We need to replenish the good bacteria in our system on a continual basis.

Anyone who has been on antibiotics needs to restore the good bacteria also known as beneficial flora.

Add probiotics to your morning smoothie, and give probiotics to your parents. Probiotics also helps the gut. Also eat some probiotic rich fermented foods every day, such as sauerkraut, fermented vegetables, fermented coconut water, coconut yogurt, kefir, and miso.

Kombucha tea is a probiotic drink that you can find in a health food supermarket. The tea is tart, but the taste buds adjust to the tartness. Many commercial brands add sugar to compensate for the tartness, look for brands with a lower sugar content.

Read Brenda Watson's book *The Road to Perfect Health* for more information about probiotics.

Salt

Most of us grew up using white refined, processed salt. White refined table salt is 98 percent sodium chloride with added bicarbonates, chemicals, sugar, and preservatives.

Companies don't have to divulge many of the ingredients in the salt on the label. Iodine is added to many refined salts. Iodine dissipates after being exposed to oxygen, so this is not a reliable source of iodine. Iodine is the main nutrient that supports our thyroid gland. White refined table salt is also lacking in numerous minerals that are in whole, natural sea salt. Many food sources today are lacking in vital dense minerals and nutrients. Soils are depleted, and refining and processing take out many or all of the nutrients in the foods.

When we sweat, our body can lose many of the minerals that are in natural, unrefined, whole sea salt, and these minerals need to be replenished. Sea salt can also help balance the body by alkalizing it. Salt is alkalizing to the body. Our pH balance is important to our health.

Salt cravings are actually a sign that you may be depleted in nutrients, minerals, and electrolytes. Salt cravings can also be a sign that your thyroid and adrenal glands are in need of minerals. If you have been craving salt or have been under a good deal of stress, it may be a good idea to have your thyroid checked to make sure you are getting enough iodine in your diet. We don't have many food sources for iodine, and it can be extremely important to our health.

Peter Ferreira conducted a two-year study of over 400 people using crystal salt. He found many benefits. In a lecture on September 8, 2001, titled "Water and Salt," he said that some benefits of ingesting crystal unrefined salt instead of refined white table salt are that it:

"Eliminates calcium deposits.

Increases usable oxygen in blood.

Un-clumps red blood cells.

Detoxifies blood.

Balances blood pressure.

Contains the full spectrum of elements that resonates with our bones and enzyme and builds bone marrow.

Neutralizes radiation (which is why nuclear waste is put into salt mines).

Makes capillaries more elastic and increases blood flow.

Adds extra electrons to the body, which are free radical scavengers.

(Electrons attach to free radicals and eliminate them. Otherwise the free radicals would contribute to hardening of the arteries and capillaries.)

Balances energy field.

Offers entire spectrum of electrolytes that the body needs.

Helps neutralize uric acid and isolated sodium chloride.

Brine water made from whole Crystal Salt has been shown to increase elimination of heavy metals through the stools.

Reduces cravings for sweets."[18]

According to a study conducted in Rotterdam, Netherlands, and reported in the *British Medical Journal* in 1994, of 100 men and women between the ages of 55 and 75 who had mild to moderate hypertension, when common table (refined) salt was replaced with mineral salt high in magnesium and potassium, a reduction in blood pressure occurred that was equivalent to blood pressure–reducing drugs.[19]

Use high-quality, mineral-rich sea salts instead of the refined types of white table salt.

> *"Whole food salts have been known to enhance health in various ways through their balanced content of minerals and trace elements. Crystal Salt is by far the most beneficial of all whole food salts because of its unique crystalline structure and the resulting life force enhancing effects. Millions of years of extreme pressure and heat have transformed sea salt into a crystalline powerhouse of life energy that far exceeds the benefits of even highest quality unrefined sea salt. In a time of widespread mineral and life energy depletion, Crystal Salt is one of the most potent measures to attain radiant health and well-being."*[20]

In conclusion, it is not that salt is bad for us; it is the type and quality of salt that is either good or bad for us.

Sprouts

Sprouts are power packed with nutrients. They have high levels of disease-preventing phytochemicals.

According to the *American Cancer Society NEWS,* "Broccoli sprouts are better for you than full-grown broccoli, and contain more of the enzyme sulforaphane which helps protect cells and prevents their genes from turning into cancer."[21] Broccoli sprouts can also have as much as 35 percent protein. One ounce of broccoli sprouts can contain as much antioxidant as 3 pounds of fully-grown broccoli! These findings are consistent with several epidemiologic studies that have shown that sprouts contain significant amounts of Vitamins A, B, C, E, and K. Sprouts are widely recognized by nutrition-conscious consumers and healthcare professionals as a wonder food.

The mung bean is the most popular sprout in Asian cuisine. Mung beans are easy to grow. Buy them in bulk at the health food store. Mung bean sprouts contain calcium, iron, magnesium, potassium, and amino acids, and are about 20 percent protein.

It's easy to learn how to grow sprouts. Try it for you, your parents, and your family.

Sprouting can be done easily in any place with water. Use a colander or a sprouting bag or a sprouting jar.

Directions:
1. Buy raw seeds in the bulk from seed companies or from a local nursery, or even the bulk aisle at the natural food grocery store. Certified organic seeds are recommended.
2. Rinse seeds in apple cider vinegar rinse for about 10 minutes to clean them (approximately 1/8 teaspoon vinegar to 1 cup of lukewarm water).
3. After you clean the seeds, soak seeds overnight (about 8 hours) in pure water.
4. Drain the water from the seeds and put them in a dark, cool place (around 70–75 degrees). Keep them slightly moist. You can cover them with a dishcloth. If you are using a sprouting jar, set it at an angle to help it drain, so it doesn't stay too wet, and also to allow some air into the jar. Keep them in darkness to replicate being down under the earth.
5. Rinse them with lukewarm water about three times a day, until they sprout (1–2 days).

6. After seeds have sprouted about a day and a half, you can set them in the sun to obtain the chlorophyll from the sun.

Notes:

1. Be careful when you are turning the sprouts. You can break the shoot, and when it's broken the seed will spoil.
2. Add sprouts to salads for the extra-vibrant nutrient value.
3. This is an easy, inexpensive way to get more nutrients into food for older people. Sprouts are easy to eat and packed with vitamins. You can even add a few to smoothies!
4. Save the water you drain from the sprouts. It's nutritious, and can be used in drinks, soups, smoothies, or on your plants.

Sugar

Sugar is one of the most harmful ingredients in our diet. Sugar is in almost all processed and fast foods. Sugar intake can lead to hypoglycemia, cardiovascular disease, weight gain, diabetes, kidney disease, high blood pressure, tooth decay, systemic infections, memory disorders, allergies, upset hormonal imbalances, and the list goes on.

Refined sugar, high-fructose corn syrup, and fructose are all hard on the body and the digestive system. Simple carbs, like refined sugar and high-fructose corn syrup (excepting fruit sugar), are more easily converted into glucose because their molecular structure breaks down faster in the stomach and small intestine. Therefore these carbs raise glucose levels in the bloodstream quite rapidly (less than 30 minutes). This quick rise in blood sugar can put a good deal of stress on the pancreas, which will try to regulate it by producing insulin to control it.

White, refined carbohydrates, sugar, and high-fructose corn syrup are read by the body as empty simple sugars. The empty sugar will also make the body pull nutrients from the body in order to process it. Sugar can feed cancer and other diseases.

Sugar can be hiding in many foods, so read lists of ingredients carefully.

Here are a few types of sweeteners that are alternatives to white refined or high-fructose corn syrup:

Agave syrup is marketed as a healthy sweetener, and many vegans use it because it is not an animal sweetener. According to Berkeley Wellness Alerts, agave is 90 percent fructose and is actually more fructose than what is used in high- fructose corn sweetener. It's marketed as "diabetic friendly," because it doesn't have as much glucose in it as other sweetener, but studies suggest that large amounts of fructose can "promote insulin resistance and have other harmful effects on the heart, and possibly the liver, too."[22] Fructose in its natural form in whole fruits and vegetables is much different than in a concentrated syrup form. It can be stressful to your liver and create the development of triglycerides. Agave also has more calories than table sugar. We don't buy agave and we ask restaurants, if they put it in their foods.

Stevia is a sweet plant from South America. Japanese food manufacturers developed this sweetener from the stevia plant in the 1970s for use in their products. The Japanese have done extensive research on stevia and found it to be safe. The less-refined varieties of stevia are the best in terms of health benefits. Stevia has no calories and low glycemic properties. This sweetener is probably one of the best choices for diabetics to use. I (Nancy) like the liquid variety best. Check carefully to see what ingredients are used in them. I (Nancy) found one that had grapefruit seed extract used as a preservative. A client of mine (Nancy) was using it, and because of his medication, this grapefruit ingredient could have killed him.

I (Nancy) like to use liquid stevia. I've found that the powder form of stevia has a kind of bitter aftertaste. I like to use the xylitol powder instead, if I need to use a packet of powder sweetener.

Honey is a natural sweetener that is anti-fungal and has anti-bacterial properties.

Xylitol is a sugar alcohol in fruits and vegetables made from birch tree bark and other hard wood trees. Finland used this sugar during World War II when they had a sugar shortage. Germany, Switzerland, Japan, and the Soviet Union were using xylitol by the 1960s extensively. It was their preferred sweetener for diabetics. Many studies have been done on xylitol; it has been shown to help prevent cavities, repair dental enamel, regulate blood sugar for those with Type 2 diabetes, strengthen bones, decrease age-related bone loss, inhibit systematic yeast problems, and inhibit the growth of bacteria that cause middle-ear infections in children, and it can inhibit the growth of strep. Xylitol has 75 percent fewer carbohydrates than sugar and fewer calories. Studies have shown that ingesting xylitol can alkalize your body, reduce sugar cravings, and reduce insulin levels. The FDA approved it in 1963.

Date sugar is sugar derived from dried dates. This type of sugar has some fiber and is rich with minerals. Since it is essentially dried fruit, it is a nice alternative to other sugars.

Maple syrup is a natural sugar derived from the maple tree sap that contains minerals.

Lakanto is made by a Japanese corporation, Saraya. Lakanto is a proprietary blend of two uniquely processed ingredients: erythritol and luo han guo (an extract from a fruit from China). They call this fruit (luo han guo) the longevity fruit, and the fruit alone is 300 times sweeter than sugar. According to the website, erythritol is a sugar alcohol produced through the fermentation of non-GMO certified corn. It was introduced in 1996. They say it looks like sugar, tastes like sugar, and cooks like sugar. It is very expensive. They advertise it as being zero calories. Donna Gates promotes it. (For more information go to her website, the Body Ecology Website.)

Chemically derived sweeteners can have a harmful effect on health. Read ingredient labels carefully, and check for any sugar or sugar substitute.

Vitamin D

Vitamin D is an essential vitamin. Studies suggest that almost 85 percent of the population is Vitamin D–deficient. This overlooked vitamin is involved in our heart, skin, aging, sleep, eye, respiratory, immune system, mood, bone muscle, and digestive health. According to studies, "**every cell and tissue *needs* vitamin D for its well-being**" and Vitamin D "regulates over 2000 genes in the body."[23] With the increase in cancer today, this vitamin could be an important part of preventing it. According to Dr. Heaney, a prominent researcher who has authored more than 400 papers on Vitamin D, "the 2007 cancer study that showed a full 77 percent of all cancers could be prevented with a vitamin D level of at least 40 ng/ml."[24]

As people age, other problems like osteoporosis become a problem. Vitamin D seems to be a key element in preventing this type of problem as well. Dr. Simon Vanlint from the University of Adelaide said, "Vitamin D plays an important role in helping the body to absorb calcium and maintain healthy bones, muscles and teeth. Vitamin D deficiency can increase a person's risk of bone and muscle pain, rickets (in children) and osteoporosis."[25] So, if you are concerned about brittle bones, make sure you have your vitamin D levels checked. "Recent studies have also suggested links between lack of vitamin D and a wide range of conditions, including diabetes, heart disease, cancer, lung disease, mental health problems, skin disorders and some auto-immune diseases."[26]

Studies show that everyone absorbs Vitamin D differently. A blood test by your physician on a regular basis is recommended, because the Vitamin D levels fluctuate during the year.

Older people tend to lose the ability to utilize and generate Vitamin D in their skin. Therefore studies show older people actually need more Vitamin D. Also, older people tend to spend more time indoors, making them prime candidates for critically low Vitamin D.

Ten to 15 minutes of direct sunlight on the skin without sunscreen has been recommended as a minimum daily requirement.

Supplements should be a whole food vitamin. There are very few foods that contain Vitamin D; a few foods that do contain some Vitamin D are parsley, eggs, liver, and some fatty fish, like cod. According to studies, lower back pain and muscle strength are improved with addition of Vitamin

D when it had been deficient. Most people think drinking milk will give them sufficient Vitamin D, but studies showed that people who drank fortified milk had similar Vitamin D levels as people who didn't drink Vitamin D–fortified milk. If you feel you may have some health problems, it may be prudent to have your Vitamin D levels checked by your physician.

Water

ater is a key nutrient to our health. We can live 40 days without food, but only three days without water. Adults are about 60 to 72 percent water. Blood uses water to transport nutrients, antibodies, and oxygen to all parts of the body. Many illnesses are a result of chronic intercellular dehydration. Most people don't get enough water, and it is a critically important nutrient for our health.

Because of the state of the municipal water supply, a water filter can be a smart purchase. Reverse Osmosis is one of the best water-filtration systems. High-quality water purification systems remove everything, removing the bad chemicals and toxins as well as the good minerals, creating empty water.

The body needs minerals when processing water. When drinking water is devoid of minerals, the body will pull minerals from the body in order to process it. There is a simple solution to this problem of empty water: If you add some minerals, such as a pinch of unrefined, pure, whole sea salt to the purified water, it will add minerals to the water. These minerals are electrolytes. Therefore, the body will not need to draw the minerals from the body to process it.

When we shower or bathe, we can absorb about eight glasses worth of water into our skin. If the water is filled with chemicals (like chlorine or fluoride), we can absorb those. If you don't have a whole house water filter, a shower filter is a good investment. You can fill up the bathtub using a shower head.

Start your mornings by squeezing the fresh juice of half a lemon or lime into a glass of warm water and drinking it on an empty stomach. This will give you a burst of Vitamin C, flush bad bacteria from the organs, and alkalize and hydrate the body. Avoid liquids with meals because they can water down the digestive enzyme juices, making it harder to digest food. Water is best between meals.

Drink a glass of water about an hour before each meal, and then drink another glass of water about two and a half hours after each meal. Drinking a half ounce of water for every pound of body weight each day is a good daily habit.

Part II
Recipes

One of the most important instructions for preparing food is to taste it as you are cooking. Adjust salt, pepper, spices, herbs, liquids, and ingredients as needed.

Smoothies and Beverages

Smoothies are power drinks. They are a great way for everyone, especially older people who may not have much of an appetite, to get needed nutrients easily.

You may want to use a powerful blender if you use nuts or whole fruits, including the peel/skin. If you have a standard blender, you may need to soak nuts before blending to keep your blender from breaking.

Various ingredients can be added to make a nutrient-dense drink. Add 1–2 tablespoons of one, two, or all of these ingredients to any smoothie:

- **Goji berries**. Soak them overnight to create a soft berry that's easy to blend.
- **Protein powder**. Use whole-grain, brown rice protein powder, hemp protein powder, or Garden of Life Protein Powder.
- **Green food powder**. There are a number of good brands. Look for a raw, organic brand. The chlorophyll is beneficial to health.
- **Aloe vera** or pure aloe vera juice.
- **Maca root powder** (raw). Maca root is one

of the only foods that supports the adrenal glands, and it helps with stress and libido.

- **Probiotics.** These help replenish the beneficial flora of the system. Probiotics can be added to the smoothie every day. Open up the capsules and pour right into the smoothie mixture.

- **Spirulina.** Spirulina, high-protein algae, is a good source of Vitamin B12, as well as Vitamins A, B1, B2, B6, D, and E.

- **Bee pollen.** Bee pollen is an excellent source of long-chain amino acid protein, is an immune system booster, and has been known to help with relief of arthritis.

- **Digestive enzymes** (organic, raw, and living). You can open the capsule and add directly into the smoothie.

- **Yogurt or kefir.** This will make a creamier consistency and be a probiotic addition to the smoothie. An organic, raw (unpasturized), unsweetened yogurt or kefir is best. "Yogurt is especially beneficial for older people, the bacteria in yogurt break down milk sugar in the intestinal tract into lactic acid in which disease –producing bacteria cannot live."[27]

- **Nut butter** (almond, cashew, sunflower seed, peanut, etc.).

- **Avocado.**
- **Nuts and seeds.** Nuts and seeds add protein, carbohydrates, and oil. They are "complete" foods. Soak almonds, cashews, walnuts, pine nuts, pumpkin seeds, and sunflower seeds for at least a couple of hours in water to make them more digestible. Soaking the nuts also helps remove the phytic acid in the nut. Phytic acid can keep the body from being able to absorb nutrients such as calcium, magnesium, iron, and zinc. Phytic acid also has digestive enzyme inhibitors. Pour off and discard the water in which the nuts have been soaked. Soaking them also makes them softer and easier to chew.
- **Omega 3 essential fatty acids** (flax seed oil, hemp oil, etc.).
- **Chia seeds** (for Omega 3 and Omega 6). Soak 1 tablespoon chia seeds in a glass of water overnight. The chia seeds will have a gelatinous consistency. Use approximately 1 tablespoon chia seeds in a smoothie.
- **Coconut oil.** Always purchase pure, organic, extra-virgin coconut oil to ensure that you are not purchasing a trans fat coconut oil. Add a teaspoon to a tablespoon of pure, extra-virgin coconut oil to smoothies.

Benefits of coconut oil include[28]:
- **Promoting your heart health.**
- **Supporting your immune system health.**
- **Supporting a healthy metabolism.**
- **Providing you with an immediate energy source.**
- **Helping to keep your skin healthy and youthful looking.**
- **Supporting the proper functioning of your thyroid gland.**

Fat helps our body process carbohydrates and proteins. Try to combine the three (fat, protein, and carbohydrates) in meals so they can work together.

You can use coconut water as the liquid in smoothies. Coconut water is extremely hydrating and full of natural electrolytes. Fruit juice can also be used as the liquid in smoothies.

Buy organic, raw nuts through the Internet from reliable sources. Most nuts sold at stores are not raw and don't contain much nutritional value. They should be refrigerated, as nuts go rancid easily. Stores should have them refrigerated, if they are raw and fresh.

vegetarian/raw

CACAO, ALMOND BUTTER, AND BANANA SMOOTHIE

Ingredients:

1 banana

1 T. almond butter

1 T. cacao powder

1 T. coconut oil (raw and organic, with or without the coconut meat)

1 T. flax seed oil (or ground-up flax seed)

2 c. milk (oat, almond, hemp, rice; whatever milk you choose)

6 drops of stevia

1 scoop protein powder

Directions:

1. Blend all ingredients until smooth.

Serving size: 1 serving

Variation: Use cashew butter instead of almond butter.

GREEN SMOOTHIES

One afternoon after lunch while I (Mary-ann) was staying at my parents' house, I went upstairs to my old bedroom and was watching Maryann Esposito on TV. She was cooking a dish with kale, and she said you can make a delicious smoothie with a banana and raw kale in the blender.

I never heard of mixing a green with a banana.

I couldn't wait to try it. I knew that was a little too radical for my parents; they draw the line at anything bright green in a drink. I waited until I went home to make the smoothie. I couldn't believe how delicious it was. I started making the banana kale smoothie every day. But I knew the banana was full of sugar and I wanted to avoid sugar, so put a little liquid stevia in the drink instead of the banana. I started experimenting with all kinds of green smoothies, I was excited to see what would happen as I dumped lettuce, celery, parsley, cucumber, zucchini, fennel, stevia, and chia seeds into my blender. The color was incredible! It was so green and pretty; I was hooked.

I looked forward to the smoothies, more than I did my morning cappuccino.

I went back to my parents' house and began giving my mother shot-glass-sized smoothies. She started drinking them. Then I gave my father a small glass. "What is it?" he asked as he looked down into the green liquid.

"I made it just for you." I smiled Carefully he lifted the glass to his lips and started to drink it. He didn't say anything, but he didn't spit it out. I was thrilled; this was a new way to get him to add more nutrients to his diet.

When you make a smoothie with raw vegetables you get all the nutrients, including fiber (unlike when ingredients are juiced, which removes fiber). Use a variety of greens, including lettuce, cucumber, celery (including the celery leaves), zucchini, fennel, parsley, mint, and whatever vegetables you have in the refrigerator.

It's easier to digest vegetables in a green smoothie, so these are especially good for older people who might have problems chewing.

Add five to eight drops of regular liquid stevia or a flavored liquid stevia, like the Sweet Leaf brand's vanilla crème, to add a little sweetness. Stevia is about 40 times sweeter than sugar and has no calories.

For more information on vegetable smoothies, go to the Body Ecology website.[29]

vegetarian/vegan/gluten-free/raw

BANANA KALE SMOOTHIE

Ingredients:
 1 banana
 3 kale leaves, without the stems
 1–2 T. water (optional)

Directions:
 1. Blend all ingredients until smooth.
 2. Add a little water, if it is too thick to drink easily.

Serving size: 1 serving

vegetarian/vegan/ gluten-free/raw

GREEN SMOOTHIE #1

Ingredients:

½ cucumber

¼ c. Italian parsley (a few sprigs)

¼ zucchini (about ¼ c.)

1 romaine lettuce leaf

1 T. pure, organic, extra-virgin coconut oil

5–8 drops stevia

2 T. chia seeds (soaked in water overnight)

½ c. water or coconut water (You can add more of the liquid as necessary to the mixture to make the smoothie easier to drink.)

Directions:

1. Blend all ingredients until creamy and smooth.

Serving size: 1 serving

vegetarian/vegan/gluten-free/raw

GREEN SMOOTHIE #2

Ingredients:

- 1 to 2 bananas
- 1 c. raspberries
- 1 Golden Delicious apple (cored, seeded, and quartered)
- ½ bunch spinach (about 2 c.)
- 1 tsp. chia seeds
- 1 tsp. pure, extra-virgin, organic coconut oil
- 3 dates or a few drops of stevia (optional, to sweeten)
- 1½ c. water or coconut water

Directions:

1. Blend all the ingredients until smooth.
2. Add a little more water as necessary, to make it more liquid-y.

Variation:

1. Substitute pear for apple.

Serving size: 2 servings

vegetarian/vegan/gluten-free/raw

MANIC MONDAY SMOOTHIE

Ingredients:
- 1 banana
- 2 heaping T. hemp protein powder
- 2 T. almond butter
- 1/3 c. chia seeds (soaked overnight in water)
- 2 leaves raw kale
- ½ c. water
- 2 probiotic capsules, opened
- 2 capsules raw, organic enzymes, opened
- 1–2 ice cubes (optional)

Directions:
1. Blend all ingredients until smooth (about 5 minutes).

Note: Do not use kale stems.

Serving size: 2 servings

vegetarian/vegan/gluten-free

RAINBOW SMOOTHIE

Ingredients:

2½ c. pure, unsweetened apple or pear juice

2 bananas

1½ c. berries (blueberries, strawberries, blackberries, raspberries, or a combination)

1 T. organic flax seed oil

1 T. pure, extra-virgin, organic coconut oil

Directions:

1. Blend all ingredients until smooth.

Variations:

1. Use cherries instead of berries.

2. Add some probiotics or 1/3 c. raw, unsweetened kefir (for a creamier consistency and additional probiotics).

Note: Fresh berries are best, but use frozen if that's all you have or all you can find.

Serving size: 2 servings

vegetarian/ vegan/gluten-free

GREEN LEMONADE

Ingredients:
1 lemon (peeled and quartered)
1 cucumber
2–3 stalks celery
1 Granny Smith apple, cored and seeded

Directions:
1. Juice all ingredients and enjoy!

Notes:
1. Add some other greens into this drink for added nutritional benefit. Some examples of good choices are kale, romaine lettuce, red leaf lettuce, and watercress.
2. Lemon rind is packed with Vitamin C and can really help cut the green flavor of greens. Use the rind if your juicer can handle it.
3. Drink freshly juiced beverages within 20 minutes to get the maximum nutritional benefit.
4. Fresh juices are a great way to get nutrition easily and quickly into the body.
5. Juicing fresh vegetables is healthy and lower in sugar than fruits.
6. Make sure all of your vegetables and fruits are clean before juicing.

Milk Alternatives[30]

Flavors and Sweeteners for Alternative Milks

For all of these milks, you can make them flavored if you wish. Here are a few ways to make them sweeter or more flavored:

1. Sweet Leaf brand stevia comes in flavors: orange, vanilla, toffee, and several others. They have no calories and are healthy. This is my (Nancy's) sweetener of choice.

2. Add a dash or more of vanilla extract, maple extract, or almond extract.

3. Add a dash of cinnamon or a little grated orange zest for a bolder flavor. Cinnamon tastes good with orange, and you can do lemon or lime as well. With lemon or lime, you may want to add a tiny bit of maple syrup, honey, or a few more dates.

4. You can make many different flavors by adding any infused water.

5. Coconut water can be used to soak the cashews and added as the water for a wonderful coconut cream. Add a tiny bit of vanilla to this mixture.

raw

ALMOND MILK

I (Nancy) use this milk for many things, including as the liquid in my smoothies. I make my milk without sweetener and then add what I need to make it sweeter, depending on what I am using it for. I like to add a few drops of stevia most of the time. To flavor nut milks for drinking or to use on granola, I like to use the toffee stevia drops by Sweat Leaf. If I am using it for a recipe, I use plain stevia. Maryann likes vanilla-flavored stevia. It is just a matter of personal opinion; find out what your favorite is!

Ingredients:

1 c. almonds, soaked in a bowl of water, refrigerated 12 to 18 hours and rinsed

3 c. water

A few drops of stevia for sweetness (optional)

Directions:

1. Blend soaked almonds with water until smooth.
2. Strain mixture through a sprout bag, cheesecloth, or strainer into a big bowl.
3. Refrigerate any milk that is not consumed.

Notes:

1. This milk will last in the refrigerator for

about three to five days. Shake well before using.

2. Save the almond pulp in a container. Put in the refrigerator or freezer for later use. I (Nancy) use it to make my raw breads and crackers.

3. Almonds are soaked in water to remove the phytic acid.

Variations:

1. For a sweeter version, take a vanilla bean, split it, and scrape out the seeds. Add the seeds to the almond milk in a blender. Then add two or three dates, or another sweetener (like stevia), and blend until smooth.

2. Use a flavored stevia (like the ones by Sweet Leaf).

3. Substitute walnuts for almonds.

raw

CASHEW CREAM OR MILK

I (Nancy) started experimenting with different nut milks and found that I really like the creamy texture of cashews. You can make all kinds of wonderful recipes with this mixture as milk. I like to soak the nuts overnight in the refrigerator, but if you soak them for a minimum of two hours, they will get soft enough to make a really nice milk when mixed in a blender. I add extra water to make it less creamy and milkier. This mixture is great with granola cereals. I try to keep a fresh mixture of this in my refrigerator at all times. I make it fresh about every three days. If you add some other flavors to it, it can make a nice cream for desserts and cereal toppings.

You can make any amount of this. This recipe makes a small amount (about 1/2 cup) to start, and you can double this recipe easily.

Ingredients:

1 c. cashews, preferably raw and organic
1 1/2 c. water (for soaking the nuts at least two
    hours or overnight)
1/2 c. water (for adding to blender)
A drop or two of stevia for sweetness

Directions:
1. Drain nuts after soaking in 1 1/2 c. water.
2. Blend nuts and 1/2 c. water in a blender until smooth and creamy.
3. Add water to the desired consistency. (Add the amount of liquid as you go. You can make it thicker, like a cream, or you can make it thinner, like milk.)
4. Refrigerate any milk you do not drink immediately.

Variations:
1. For a sweeter cream, add a date or two with the pit removed that have been soaked in just enough water to cover at least 30 minutes. Always add soaking water to the blender with the dates.
2. For a sweet flavor, add Sweet Leaf brand stevia sweetener, which comes in many flavors. It has no calories and is healthy. This is my (Nancy's) sweetener of choice. In this cream, I love the toffee flavor. Vanilla is also really good.
3. Add a dash of vanilla extract, maple extract, or almond extract.
4. Add a tablespoon or more of fruit juice, like apple juice with a dash of cinnamon

or orange juice (with a grated zest of the rind for a bolder flavor). Cinnamon tastes good with the orange flavor; you could do lemon or lime as well. With the lemon or lime, you may want to add a tiny bit of maple syrup, honey, or a few more dates.

raw

OAT MILK

This is very much like rice milk, only I (Nancy) use raw, uncooked oats. I use non-flavored stevia and omit vanilla if I am using the oat milk in a recipe.

Ingredients:
1/2 c. raw whole oats
Stevia to taste
1 1/2 c. water
Dash of sea salt
1 vanilla bean

Directions:
1. Soak oats for 12 hours in 1 cup of the water called for in the ingredients list. This will help remove the phytic acid. Pour off any water when finished soaking.
2. Split vanilla bean and use a sharp knife to scrape out the inside of the bean. Put the scrapings in a blender.
3. Combine all the ingredients in a blender and blend well.
4. Strain through a nut milk bag or simply drink as a thicker, more fiber-filled version.
5. Refrigerate any milk you do not drink right away.

Variations:

1. Add more oats for a thicker milk.
2. Use an alternative vanilla flavor for this milk, such as a drop or two of vanilla-flavored stevia.
3. Add a handful or a few tablespoons of pine nuts or walnuts for a richer flavor.

raw

PINE NUT MILK

This is very much like rice milk, only using pine nuts. This is a thin nut milk, but you can add a few more nuts to make it thicker. Mediterranean pine nuts have more protein in them than any other nut. Pine nuts also have a unique ability to make you feel full and satisfied. They are great to have in your diet if you need weight control. They can be expensive, but a little goes a long way.

Ingredients:
1 vanilla bean
1 1/2 c. water
1/2 c. raw pine nuts,
Dash of sea salt
Stevia to taste (a drop or two)

Directions:
1. Split the vanilla bean and use a sharp knife to scrape out the inside of the bean. Put scrapings in blender.
2. Combine all ingredients in a blender and blend well.
3. Strain through a nut milk bag, or simply drink.

Variation:

Omit the vanilla bean or use an alternative vanilla flavor. I (Nancy) love toffee-flavored liquid stevia in this drink.)

raw

RICE MILK

I (Nancy) started experimenting with alternative milks because I couldn't find ones in the supermarket that were organic and/or not filled with sugar. This has become one of my absolute favorites. I do sometimes use rice that is from the refrigerator, but freshly cooked rice is best.

Ingredients:
- 1 vanilla bean
- 1 c. whole-grain rice (freshly cooked)
- 2 c. water
- Stevia to taste
- Dash of sea salt

Directions:
1. Split the vanilla bean and use a sharp knife to scrape out the inside of the bean. Put the scrapings in a blender.
2. Combine all ingredients in a blender and blend well.
3. Strain through a nut milk bag, or simply drink it as a thicker version. (The more rice you add, the thicker the milk will be.)

Notes:
1. Omit or use an alternative vanilla flavor for this milk. Toffee-flavored stevia (by Sweet Leaf) is one I (Nancy) sometimes

use instead of the vanilla bean.

2. Honey or brown rice syrup works well as a sweetener.

raw

VEGAN EGG NOG

This is an easy version of egg nog. It makes a nice holiday drink!

Ingredients:

    1 1/2 c. vanilla-flavored, almond, hazelnut, or rice milk

    1 banana

    Pinch of nutmeg

    A few drops stevia (optional)

Directions:

1. Place all ingredients in a blender and blend until creamy.

Note: This recipe is easy to double.

Alive and Cooking:
An Easy Guide to Health for You and Your Parents

Breakfast Recipes

Before breakfast we (Maryann's family) gave my dad Floradix, a liquid multi-vitamin; it has a fruity flavor and tastes good. My mother mixed it with juice.

We also gave my dad a one-egg omelet. "Egg yolks are one of the finest foods for the nervous system. The part of the egg yolk which is good for the nervous system is called vitellin. Vitellin goes along with lecithin. Lecithin is a brain and nerve fat, and it is also found in egg yolk. Egg yolk is a far richer source of lecithin than any other food."[31]

vegetarian/gluten-free

BASIC OMELET

Ingredients:

5 fresh, organic eggs

3 T. cow's milk, goat's milk, or almond milk

Sea salt to taste

Pepper to taste

2 T. pure, extra-virgin, organic coconut oil

1 tsp. organic butter or ghee

Directions:

1. Beat eggs in a bowl.

2. Add milk, and whisk until smooth.

3. Add salt and pepper.

4. Heat a skillet with coconut oil in it.

5. When oil is melted, add the egg mixture. It will start to solidify.

6. Gently lift the edges and let the mixture that is still liquid run down under the edges to the pan.

7. Add a little butter to the pan. (It gives it just a hint of the butter flavor, if all you have used up until this point is the coconut oil.) Lift up the edge and add it at various places around the pan in order to get an even flavor to the whole omelet.

8. As it begins to become solid, gently lift up

the edges and see if the bottom is getting a toasty golden brown color. As the bottom gets toasty brown in color and the top has no liquid left, it is about ready.

9. Gently fold the egg mixture in half and then slide onto a plate. Sprinkle with salt and pepper again, if desired.

Note: Use about two to three eggs for each person. You can adjust the recipe as needed.

Variations:

1. Add some grated cheese to the omelet after you have folded it over and are ready to take off the heat.

2. Sprinkle freshly minced parsley on top to make a beautiful presentation. (Parsley has Vitamin D in it and also cleanses the breath.)

3. Sauté chopped tomatoes and/or onion for a few minutes in the oil before adding the egg mixture. Remove vegetables from skillet, cook the egg mixture as directed, and, when the eggs are almost firm and ready to fold, add vegetables back to the omelet and then fold.

4. Sprinkle grated cheese on the egg mixture right before folding in half. Dutch cheeses,

cheddar, and Wisconsin cheeses are all good cheeses to use. (It's best to buy fresh, high-quality, organic raw cheese.)

Serving size: 2 servings

vegetarian/gluten-free

MARYANN'S QUICK AND EASY HOT AND SPICY EGGS

This is a recipe I (Maryann) made for my father, that he enjoyed. For him, the spicier the food, the more he enjoyed it. I didn't get the gene for spicy food. I am a total wimp when it comes to spicy food, but I do like this recipe.

Ingredients:

1-½ cups or 1 16-ounce jar medium hot
    chunky salsa
1 clove garlic, minced
2 T. organic coconut oil
4 eggs
sea salt to taste
pepper to taste
5–6 slices whole-grain gluten- free toast

Directions:

1. Sauté garlic and oil in a skillet over medium heat.
2. Add salsa and simmer for 3 to 5 minutes.
3. Make a well for each egg, in the salsa
4. Add one egg in each well.
5. Gently lift egg as it is cooking, to make sure it is not sticking.
6. Cook egg 2 to 3 minutes or longer, if you

like you egg more well-done.

7. When you feel like the yolk is just cooked, but still runny, gently lift the egg out and place on a plate or a piece of whole-grain toast.

8. Spoon the salsa mixture around the eggs.

9. Salt and pepper to taste.

Serving size: 2 servings

vegetarian/vegan/gluten-free/raw

CHIA SEED PUDDING

This is a delicious alternative to oatmeal. It's wonderful in the summer when cool, light food is best.

Ingredients:

1 c. chia seeds

4 c. + 3 T. water, divided

½ c. cashews

4–8 drops stevia (vanilla or toffee flavored is good)

Fresh berries (optional), rinsed and drained

Directions:

1. Soak chia seeds in 3 cups of water overnight in the refrigerator.

2. Soak cashews in 1 cup of water overnight in the refrigerator. In the morning, pour off the water.

3. Blend cashews and 3 T. fresh water in a blender. (Use less water to keep it thick.) Add a few drops of stevia to the mixture to sweeten.

4. The soaked chia seeds will become thick. This is the pudding.

5. Serve it in a bowl. Put a dollop of cashew crème on top.

6. Add some fresh berries to the mix, if using, and enjoy.

Variations:

1. Add a tablespoon of honey or maple syrup instead of stevia.
2. Add ½ teaspoon of vanilla or almond extract for more flavor.
3. Add banana in addition to or in combination with the berries, if using.

Notes:

1. Add stevia a little at a time. It's easy to add more, but it is impossible to remove if you add too much.
2. I (Nancy) like to use the toffee flavored Sweet Leaf brand stevia.
3. I (Maryann) use Sweet Leaf vanilla crème.

Serving size: 4 servings

vegetarian/gluten-free

FETA AND CAULIFLOWER OMELET

Nancy and I (Maryann) found a delicious goat feta cheese made by Patches of Star that's sold at the Union Square farmers' market in New York City that is wonderful in this recipe.

Ingredients:

5 eggs
¼ tsp. unrefined sea salt
¼ tsp. pepper (freshly ground)
2½ T. pure, extra-virgin, organic coconut oil
3 c. cauliflower florets
½ c. (about 2 oz.) feta, crumbled
¼ c. parsley (fresh)

Directions:

1. Beat eggs with sea salt and pepper.
2. Heat oil in a skillet, and sauté cauliflower florets until browned and tender, about 8 minutes.
3. Reduce heat to medium, and pour eggs over cauliflower.
4. Cook, lifting edges to let uncooked eggs run underneath and shaking skillet occasionally to loosen omelet, until set, 5–8 minutes.
5. Slide out onto a large plate.
6. Garnish with feta and parsley.

Serving size: 2 servings

vegetarian

FRENCH TOAST WITH PEANUT BUTTER AND BANANA

Ingredients:

2 eggs

¼ tsp. vanilla

2 T. orange juice

1 banana, sliced lengthwise

2 slices whole-grain bread

3 T. peanut butter

2–3 T. pure, extra-virgin, organic coconut oil

Maple syrup to taste

Directions:

1. Mix eggs, vanilla, and orange juice.
2. Spread bread slices with peanut butter.
3. Add two long slices of banana on top of peanut butter on one slice of bread.
4. Place the other bread slice on top, making a sandwich.
5. Melt coconut oil in a skillet.
6. Dip the sandwich in the egg mixture.
7. When oil is hot, place the sandwich in skillet and let it brown. (Don't let it burn.)
8. Add maple syrup as desired.

Serving size: 1–2 servings

Note: To increase the serving size of this recipe,

increase the number of slices of bread and the amount of peanut butter.

vegetarian/vegan/gluten-free/raw

GREEN PUDDING

Ingredients:

  1 ripe mango
  1 large, raw Swiss chard leaf, stems removed, torn into small pieces

Directions:

  1. Blend ingredients in a blender for a few minutes, until smooth.

Serving size: 1 serving

vegetarian/vegan/gluten-free/raw

HOMEMADE GRANOLA

Start this recipe at least one day, before you want to serve it.

Diversify this recipe to suit your taste, and/or adjust the ingredients based on what's in season. This recipe makes about 5 cups.

Ingredients:

½ c. almonds

½ c. sunflower seeds

½ c. walnuts

1 c. oats (gluten free and raw)

½ c. fresh or dried coconut (shredded)

1 c. apricots (dried)

1 c. cherries (dried)

1 c. raisins, soaked in water until plump

¼ tsp. cinnamon

¼ tsp. stevia (optional)

Fresh fruit (for example, a banana, an apple, or fresh berries), cut into small pieces (optional)

1– cups of vanilla milk (dairy, almond, coconut, or oat milk)

Directions:

1. Soak the hardest nuts, like the almonds, in water for two hours or more to make them softer and easier to chew, and to help them

become more digestible. Drain off the water. Let the nuts dry.

2. Chop the nuts and seeds into pieces. (Alternatively, use a coffee bean grinder, but only pulse it. Don't grind it to a powder; let the nuts stay in small pieces.)

3. Soak the dried fruits for about an hour to soften them, and then cut into pieces.

4. Combine all ingredients in a bowl, except fresh fruit.

5. When you are ready to serve and eat this granola, add fresh fruit, if using.

6. Serve with milk.

Notes:

1. You can store this mixture in the refrigerator or freezer for a week or longer.

2. When buying oats, read on the package if you wish to know if they are gluten free. Oats can become contaminated by gluten, if they are stored or shipped in the same facility as wheat or other glutenous grains.

vegetarian/gluten-free

QUINOA WITH APPLE

Ingredients:

2 c. purified water

1 c. organic, whole-grain quinoa

1 vanilla bean, split, scraped, and left open

¼ c. organic unsweetened almond milk

1 apple, cored, and grated

1 tsp. honey or a few drops of stevia to
   sweeten (optional)

¼ tsp. cinnamon

Unrefined sea salt to taste

Directions:

1. Place water and freshly rinsed quinoa in a pot.
2. Bring to a boil.
3. Add a dash of sea salt.
4. Reduce to a simmer and cover for about 10–15 minutes or until all water is absorbed into the quinoa.
5. Add vanilla bean
6. Add almond milk and stir.
7. Remove from heat.
8. Mix in grated apple and honey, if using.
9. Sprinkle with cinnamon.

Variations:
1. Substitute dried fruits for apple. Soak in water, chop and add to the mixture. Apricots, cherries, peaches, pineapple, and cranberries are great choices.
2. Add chopped walnuts (or pecans or almonds) for a wonderful flavor addition to the mixture.

Serving size: 2 servings (about ½ cup each)

SCRAMBLED EGGS WITH SAUTÉED SPINACH

Ingredients:

2 organic eggs

2 T. milk

Sea salt and pepper to taste

2 T. extra-virgin, pure, organic coconut oil

1 T. chopped red onion

½ cup baby spinach

Directions:

1. Crack eggs into a bowl.
2. Add milk and beat with a fork or whisk.
3. Add a little sea salt and pepper, if desired.
4. Melt oil in a frying pan and add chopped onion and sauté a moment.
5. Add spinach to the onion mixture and sauté for a minute.
6. Add the eggs to the spinach and onion mixture and stir gently.
7. Don't cook too long. As soon as the eggs get firm, take them out and put them on a plate.
8. Serve warm.

Note: Eggs beat up better if they are room temperature.

Variations:

1. Serve with a half tomato and/or whole grain toast.
2. In Texas, we like to serve salsa with our egg dishes. We also like to wrap the scrambled egg mixture in warm tortillas and serve them with the salsa as breakfast wraps. I (Nancy) recommend using whole, sprouted grain tortillas for this.

vegetarian/vegan/gluten-free

STARLIGHT PORRIDGE

Ingredients:
1 c. oats (gluten- free)

2 tsp. vanilla

2 tsp. cinnamon

¼ c. raisins

¼ tsp. sea salt

1–2 c. almond, rice, or unsweetened coconut milk

¼ c. water

Directions:
1. Combine oats, vanilla, cinnamon, raisins, salt, and milk in a bowl. Cover and refrigerate overnight.

2. The next morning, put the oat mixture in a pot with ¼ c. water

3. Simmer 20 minutes.

Serving size: 2 servings

vegetarian

WHOLE-GRAIN TOAST WITH HONEY AND CINNAMON

Honey has healing properties, cinnamon is warming and stimulates the blood, and whole-grain toast adds fiber to the diet, acts like a broom in the intestines, and helps give a full feeling.

I (Nancy) buy sprouted, whole-grain breads and ones that have more than one grain in the ingredient list. The ingredients list must say "whole grain." If it says enriched or refined, do not buy it. (That means the nutrients have been taken out or had to be added back in.) Sprouted grain bread is easier to digest and has more nutrients in it.

I (Maryann) buy "The Baker" breads. They are gluten and yeast free. My doctor recommended them for a candida-free diet.

Many grains are healthy and full of nutrients. Teff and quinoa are wonderful grains. Bread with a combination of grains can have a richer flavor. Quinoa has complex amino acids in it. It's a complete protein and is gluten free. Grains that don't have gluten in them are much easier on the body. Many people are allergic to gluten and don't even know it.

Ingredients:

Whole-grain bread, sliced and toasted

Raw honey to taste

Cinnamon to taste

Directions:
1. Drizzle honey on toasted bread.
2. Sprinkle cinnamon on top.
3. Serve warm.

vegetarian/gluten-free

YOGURT AND BERRIES

I (Nancy) make yogurt parfaits. Layer the yogurt, then fruit.

These are really nice to serve on special occasions or when you have company.

Ingredients:

1¼ c. yogurt, unsweetened plain or vanilla
1 c. berries (strawberries (sliced), blueberries, raspberries, or blackberries)
1 banana (sliced about ¼-inch thick)

Directions:

1. Take two tall clear drinking glasses or bowls (if you are using a drinking glass, use one with a stem) and put about ¼ cup of yogurt into each glass or bowl.

2. Place ¼ of the banana slices evenly over the yogurt in a thin layer.

3. Place ¼ cup of berries on top of the banana in the glasses or bowls.

4. Place another ¼ cup of yogurt on top of the berries in each glass or bowl. (Save the remaining ¼ cup to put a dollop on the top of the parfait, to make a prettier presentation)

5. Place the remaining banana slices over the yogurt in a thin layer.

6. Place another ¼ cup of berries on top of the yogurt in each glass or bowl. (Save two of the prettiest berries to put on top.)
7. Dollop the remaining ¼ cup yogurt on the top of each glass. This makes a beautiful presentation. Put one berry on top to finish it.
8. Refrigerate until ready to serve.

Note: My (Maryann's) doctor recommends eating whole-milk yogurt, not low-fat or non-fat. He says it's more nutritious to eat the complete food. He also recommends eating goat's milk or sheep's milk yogurt.

Variations:
1. Substitute kefir for yogurt.
2. Substitute any sliced fruit for berries.
3. Add granola to make a more filling breakfast.
4. Add 1 teaspoon flax seed oil for Omega 3 benefits. Combine it well with the yogurt before preparing the parfait glasses.

Serving size: 2 servings

Main Dishes

"Lunch can be the main meal of the day. Often at mid-day my father had the best appetite and he could eat a big meal."

~ Maryann De Leo

Seafood

gluten-free

BROILED FISH WITH HERBS

Ingredients:

- 3 T. pure olive oil
- 3 T. butter or ghee, melted
- ½ tsp. parsley
- ½ tsp. thyme
- ½ tsp. oregano
- Sea salt to taste (about 1 tsp.)
- Pepper to taste (about ½ tsp.)
- 1 6-oz. filet of wild caught Pacific salmon, halibut, or flounder
- 2 T. lemon juice

Directions:

1. Combine olive oil, butter, and herbs, and make a paste.

2. Rub fish with half of the olive oil, butter, and herb mixture. Set the other half aside.

3. Place fish in a broiler pan and dot the top with about a tablespoon of oil, butter and herb mixture.

4. Place fish under a 400 degree F broiler. Make sure the fish is close enough to the flame to brown, but not burn. Watch it closely. It should take about 4–6 minutes.

5. After the fish browns, turn it over, reduce

the oven temperature to 300 degrees F, dot the top of fish with another tablespoon of oil, butter, and herb mixture, and cook until tender. (If you put in a fork and it is tender and flaky, then it is ready.) This should take about 15–20 minutes.

6. Remove from heat and place on a platter.
7. Spread remaining olive oil, butter, and herb mixture over fish.
8. Drizzle lemon juice over top to serve.

Note: Garnish with thin slices of lemon and fresh parsley.

Serving size: 1 serving

SCALLOPS, COD, OR FLOUNDER IN PANKO

Ingredients:

10 medium-sized scallops **OR** 2–3 cod or flounder filets

¼ c. organic, whole-grain flour (quinoa is a good choice)

1 egg, beaten

½ c. whole-grain panko, seasoned with sea salt and pepper

4 T. pure, extra-virgin, organic coconut oil

Directions:

1. Heat coconut oil in a large frying pan.

2. Dip scallops or fish in flour, then in egg, then in Panko.

3. Cook scallops or dish in hot coconut oil. Let each side brown before turning over. (It takes just a few minutes on each side, depending on the thickness of the fish.)

4. Serve warm.

Note: When I (Maryann) made fish (or chicken or vegetables) for my father, I cut it into small pieces with scissors. The small pieces were easier for him to eat because it requires less breathing. His breathing was difficult due to emphysema.

Serving size: 3 servings

SHRIMP AND VEGETABLE TEMPURA

Ingredients:

- 1½ c. organic, whole-grain pastry flour
- 1 heaping tsp. cornstarch
- ¼ tsp. salt
- 1¼ c. water
- ½ lb. jumbo shrimp
- 1 sweet potato, washed, peeled, and cut into 1-inch slices
- 1 sweet onion, peeled and sliced into ¼-inch slices
- ½ lb. mushrooms, washed and stems removed
- 1 zucchini, washed and sliced into ¼-inch slices
- 1 c. broccoli florets, in 1-inch pieces
- 1½ c. or more extra-virgin, organic, pure coconut oil or sesame oil (or a mixture of the two combined)

Directions:

1. Mix flour, cornstarch, and salt.
2. Add half of water and mix. When mixed, add the rest of the water. (It's okay if it's lumpy.)
3. Put 3 inches of oil in a pan and heat. (Oil should be hot enough so that when battered shrimp and vegetables hit the pan, they sink to the bottom and then rise quickly.)

4. Coat each shrimp and vegetable with flour mixture.
5. Gently place shrimp and vegetables into the hot oil (the shrimp should sizzle when dropped into the oil.) and let them brown on both sides.
6. Remove shrimp and vegetables from oil and drain on paper towels.
7. Serve warm.

Notes:
1. For best results, keep the flour mixture cold and use cold vegetables.
2. Button mushrooms work well.
3. A combination of coconut oil and sesame oil works really well. It will give the dish a little sesame flavor, but the coconut oil is better with heat and is so healthy.
4. Serve this with wheat-free tamari.
5. Buy fresh, wild caught shrimp from the U.S. only.

Variation: Use any vegetable combination, including peppers and eggplant.
Serving size: 2 servings

gluten-free

WILD SALMON WITH LEMON AND DILL

Ingredients:

  1 T. pure, organic coconut oil
  4 carrots, sliced
  2 yellow squash, sliced
  4 6-oz. wild salmon steaks
  ¼ c. lemon juice
  ¼ c. butter, melted
  1½ tsp. dill
  1 tsp. lemon thyme
  1 shallot, minced
  Salt to taste
  Pepper to taste

Directions:

1. Preheat the oven to 400 degrees F.
2. Brush a medium baking dish with coconut oil.
3. Layer the bottom of the dish with carrots and squash.
4. Place salmon on top of vegetables.
5. In a medium bowl, combine lemon juice, butter, dill, lemon thyme, shallot, salt, and pepper.
6. Gently pour mixture over salmon.
7. Tightly cover baking dish and place in oven.

8. Bake 25–30 minutes, until salmon just flakes with a fork.

Notes:

1. Garnish with sprigs of fresh lemon herbs or parsley.
2. This pairs nicely with whole-grain rice.

Variation: Lemon pepper is a nice addition.

Serving size: 4 servings

gluten-free

WILD SALMON STEAKS

Ingredients:

4 wild salmon steaks
4 cloves garlic, minced
¼ c. pure olive oil
Juice of 1 lemon
Sea salt to taste
Ground black pepper to taste

Directions:

1. Rinse steaks and pat dry with a clean towel. (Don't cook wet salmon steaks.)
2. Place salmon in a baking dish.
3. In a small bowl, whisk garlic, olive oil, and lemon juice until emulsified.
4. Pour mixture over salmon, lifting steaks so that mixture covers bottoms of the steaks.
5. Let salmon marinate 30–60 minutes.
6. Remove garlic right before cooking.
7. Heat a grill pan.
8. Place salmon in the grill pan and cook 3–5 minutes per side, until cooked through.
9. Season with salt and pepper to taste.

Note: Garnish with parsley and sliced lemon.
Variation: Substitute lime for lemon.
Serving size: 4 servings

Beef, Lamb, and Poultry

gluten-free

CHICKEN IN TOMATO

Ingredients:
6 T. pure olive oil
6 cloves garlic
12 pieces organic chicken (thighs and legs)
Sea salt to taste
Black pepper to taste
2 tsp. oregano
1 12-oz. can whole plum Italian tomatoes

Directions:
1. Heat a large skillet.
2. Add olive oil.
3. Sauté garlic, but don't let it brown.
4. Season chicken with salt and pepper.
5. Add chicken to skillet. Let chicken pieces brown before turning. When browned on one side (about 4 minutes), turn chicken over and brown the other side.
6. Remove chicken from the pan.
7. Add oregano and tomatoes to the same pan.
8. Let it cook about 15 minutes.
9. Return chicken to the pan.
10. Allow chicken to cook about 30 minutes over low heat.
11. Season with salt to taste.

Note: Serve this with noodles, quinoa, or rice.

gluten-free

CHICKEN IN WINE

Ingredients:

3 T. olive oil (or pure, extra-virgin, organic coconut oil)

1 onion, thinly sliced

4 c. white wine (not cooking wine)

12 organic skinless chicken thighs (or 2¾ lb. thigh filets)

2 c. mushrooms, sliced thin

Unrefined sea salt to taste

Freshly ground pepper to taste

Directions:

1. Heat oil in a casserole or large, wide pan.
2. Sauté onion until soft.
3. Add wine.
4. Gently place chicken thighs and mushrooms in pan.
5. Season with salt and pepper, and bring to a boil.
6. Cover pan and simmer gently for an hour.

Notes:

1. Serve this over buttered noodles, quinoa, or rice.
2. This is a good recipe for refrigerating and enjoying as a leftover.

3. I (Maryann) buy kosher organic chicken.
4. Riesling is a good choice for wine in this recipe.

Serving size: 5–6 servings

SHISH KEBABS

Ingredients:

2 lb. beef sirloin, boneless lamb, or skinless
chicken breast, cut into 1½-inch cubes

Teriyaki sauce

1 large red onion, cut into big squares

2 zucchini, thickly sliced

1½ c. cherry tomatoes (whole), about 1 pound

1 lb. mushrooms, stems removed

1 pineapple, cut into 1-inch cubes

Unrefined sea salt to taste

Pepper to taste

Extra-virgin, pure, organic coconut oil

9–12 skewers

Directions:

1. If you are using an outdoor grill, start the
   fire. (Skewers can also be baked or broiled
   in the oven or grilled on an electric indoor
   grill.)

2. Place meat in a dish so the teriyaki sauce
   completely covers it. Refrigerate for an
   hour or two, turning the meat over every
   once in a while to make sure the meat is
   thoroughly marinated.

3. Rub skewers with coconut oil.

4. Assemble shish kebabs. Put onions, meat,
   then pineapple, tomatoes, meat, mush-

rooms, and zucchini. Continue until skewer is filled.

5. Put shish kebabs in a large zip-top baggie with teriyaki sauce. Refrigerate until ready to cook. (Do this at least an hour in advance.)

6. Bake, broil, or grill shish kebabs on medium heat for about 10 minutes, or until meat is done the way you like it. Turn the shish kebabs over every few minutes so they cook evenly. Make sure they don't burn.

Variations:

1. For a vegetarian version, use seitan or wheat meat in a comparable one-to-one conversion.

2. Marinate seitan and/or mushroom for vegetarian guests in a separate dish from meat.

Notes:

1. If using wood skewers, soak in water for 20–30 minutes before using.

2. Brush with marinade while the kebabs are cooking for a nice glaze.

3. Always use organic, grass-fed beef, lamb, or chicken.

Serving size: approximately 9 servings

Vegetarian

vegetarian/vegan (if you don't use the cheese)/gluten-free

BEANS AND RICE WITH VEGETABLES

Ingredients:
- 2 T. extra-virgin, pure, organic coconut oil
- 1 onion (2/3 c.), chopped
- 3 small tomatoes, chopped
- 1 zucchini, chopped
- 1¼ c. beans, cooked
- 1 tsp. oregano (dried or fresh)
- 1–2 cloves garlic, minced
- Sea salt to taste
- Pepper to taste
- 3 c. whole medium-grain brown rice, cooked and warm
- 2 c. cheese (optional)

Directions:
1. Heat oil in a skillet.
2. Add onion and sauté until soft.
3. Add tomatoes and zucchini, and sauté 6–7 minutes.
4. Add beans, oregano, garlic, salt, and pepper, and sauté until warm.
5. Serve this mixture over the rice.
6. Sprinkle with cheese, if using, and serve warm.

Notes:

1. The cheese sprinkled on top will add another layer of rich flavor, and it looks pretty as well. Pick any sharp cheese you like.

2. Just about any variety of whole-grain brown rice will work for this recipe. One cup of uncooked rice will make about 3 cups of cooked rice.

3. Add the garlic at the end. It's fragile and the medicinal properties can be hurt by heat. Sometimes I (Nancy) add half to my dish after I have finished the cooking process to make sure it is still potent.

Serving size: 4 servings

vegetarian

BUCKWHEAT PASTA WITH CHEESE, POTATOES, CABBAGE, AND SAGE

Ingredients:

1 red onion, chopped

6 T. butter

3 cloves garlic, minced

2 T. fresh sage leaves (about 4)

½ tsp. sea salt, plus more to taste

1 potato, cubed

1 c. cabbage, shredded

½ lb. buckwheat pasta

1 c. Fontina cheese, grated

1 c. Parmesan cheese, grated

Pepper to taste

1 cup whole-grain bread crumbs

Directions:

1. Bring a large pot of water to a boil.

2. In a large skillet, sauté onion in butter until onion is slightly translucent.

3. Add the garlic and sage for and cook for just a minute, and remove from heat.

4. Add sea salt, potatoes, and cabbage to the pot of boiling water. Cook until potatoes are tender.

5. Add pasta and cook until the pasta is ready

(about 5–8 minutes).

6. Drain pasta, potatoes, and cabbage.
7. In an oven-proof dish, spread a layer of vegetables, then pasta.
8. Add a layer of Fontina cheese, and then a layer of Parmesan. Sprinkle with salt and pepper.
9. Continue layering until all ingredients are used, ending with a layer of Parmesan.
10. Cover with whole-grain bread crumbs, drizzle with butter and sage, and discard garlic.
11. Bake at 350 degrees for 15 minutes, or until golden brown on top and cheese has melted.

Variation: Buckwheat flat, broad (pizzoccheri) pasta is traditional, but you can use whole-grain pasta noodles. Fettuccine works well.

Note: Savoy is a delicious type of cabbage to use.

Serving size: 4 servings

vegetarian/vegan/gluten-free

FALAFEL

Occasionally I (Nancy) like to eat fried food. Growing up in Texas with Southern cooking, this is comfort food for me. I like the crispy, crunchy, warm food with a rich inside middle. It reminds me of home. Even though we didn't cook Indian food often, my father loved spices and trying foods from all over the world. This is a protein-rich dish that can be eaten alone, or with soup, bread, or crackers.

Ingredients:

1½ c. chickpeas (3½ c. cooked)

1 or 2 inches kombu seaweed (for cooking the chickpeas)

1 red onion, chopped

5 cloves fresh garlic, minced

3 T. fresh lemon juice

1 chipotle pepper, minced

1½ c. fresh parsley

1½ tsp. unrefined, sea salt

1 tsp. freshly ground black pepper

2 tsp. cumin, ground

2 tsp. coriander seeds, freshly ground

1 c. whole-grain quinoa flour

Pure, organic extra-virgin coconut oil for frying

Directions:

1. Soak chickpeas overnight in water.

2. Drain chickpeas and then place in a pot of water (water should be at least 1 inch over the top of the chickpeas) and bring to a boil.

3. Drain water and refill the pot with the chickpeas and enough water to cover them by at least one inch. Add a pinch of salt and the seaweed to the pot, and bring to a boil again.

4. Turn down heat and simmer for about an hour, until chickpeas are tender. Remove from the heat and drain off the water. Remove the seaweed if you desire.

5. Place chickpeas, onion, garlic, lemon juice, chipotle pepper, parsley, salt, pepper, cumin, and coriander seeds in a food processor, and pulse until it makes a nice, combined dough.

6. Make small balls out of the dough, and gently flatten slightly (a little under ½ inch in thickness and not too large; you want them to cook quickly).

7. Heat the coconut oil in a frying pan.

8. Gently place balls into the whole grain quinoa flour and coat.

9. Gently place flour-covered balls into hot oil and cook each side until lightly brown.

10. Remove from heat and place on a plate with paper towels to soak up oil.

11. Serve warm.

vegetarian/gluten-free

KITCHRI (RICE AND LENTILS)

Ingredients:

½ lb. whole grain rice

½ lb. small French lentils

4–6 oz. butter

4–6 cloves garlic, chopped

1 T. tomato puree

water

Sea salt to taste

Directions:

1. Wash rice and lentils separately and soak in cold water: rice for 30 minutes; lentils for 1 hour.

2. Melt half the butter in a saucepan.

3. Gently sauté garlic for 2–3 minutes.

4. Mix in drained rice and lentils, so grains are cooked with garlic and butter.

5. Add tomato puree and mix.

6. Add water to cover rice and lentils by about ½ inch.

7. Add salt to taste.

8. Bring to a boil over high heat.

9. Reduce heat to medium and allow liquid to be absorbed.

10. When only a few bubbles remain on the surface, reduce the heat to a minimum, cover tightly, and steam for about 15 minutes.

Variations:

1. Garnish with sliced onions, sliced tomatoes and cheese, onion rings fried in butter, or slices of cheese fried in butter. (Haloumi is ideal for taste and texture. It does not disintegrate in cooking and only melts slighty. Goat cheese or cheddar work, too.)

2. Fry 2 or 3 more minced garlic cloves in butter in a separate pan and add before serving.

Note: Basmati rice is a great choice for this recipe.

Serving size: 4 servings

vegetarian

NANCY'S BROCCOLI QUICHE

Use a pre-made, organic, whole-grain crust from the frozen foods section of the grocery store. This is a great dish to make if you are having company. It's easy to double the recipe and make two at a time.

Ingredients:

1 whole-grain pie crust

¼ c. onion, chopped

1 tsp. organic, extra-virgin, pure coconut oil

1 c. broccoli florets (cut into bite-sized florets)

1 c. organic milk

½ tsp. parsley (dried or freshly minced)

½ tsp. chives (dried or freshly minced)

¼–½ tsp. unrefined sea salt

¼ tsp. pepper

3 eggs, well beaten

1 tsp. mustard

1 c. organic cheddar cheese, grated

½ c. organic mozzarella cheese, grated

Directions:

1. Preheat the oven to 350 degrees F.
2. Sauté onion and coconut oil until onion is slightly soft and translucent.
3. Add broccoli and sauté another few minutes.

4. Mix together milk, parsley, chives, salt, pepper, and eggs, and set aside.

5. Spread mustard evenly around the base of the pie crust.

6. Spread the broccoli mixture evenly around pie crust over mustard.

7. Combine cheeses and sprinkle evenly over broccoli.

8. Pour egg mixture over cheese and broccoli.

9. Bake 30–45 minutes, until top is golden brown and pie seems firm. (Stick a toothpick in the center to see if it comes out clean. If it seems firm, it is ready.)

10. Remove from the oven and let stand at least 5 minutes before cutting.

Variations:

1. If you aren't an onion lover, omit it or use 1 T. grated onion. (If using grated onion, disregard the sautéing step. Just add it when mixing the egg mixture.)

2. Substitute asparagus tips or spinach for broccoli.

3. Use different cheeses like Monterey Jack. (I (Nancy) like to use a chipotle cranberry cheese to give the quiche a little kick!)

4. Use almond, rice, or goat milk instead of

cow's milk.

5. Substitute spicy, hot mustard if that is your preference. Don't over-use the mustard.

Note: Use cheese that has vegetarian enzymes instead of the rennet, if you want the quiche to be vegetarian.

Serving size: 4–6 servings

vegetarian/gluten-free (if you use a gluten-free pasta)

PASTA WITH FRESH TOMATOES

Ingredients:

1 c. whole-grain pasta

3 large tomatoes, chopped

1 T. fresh basil, chopped

2 T. extra-virgin olive oil

Unrefined sea salt to taste

Pepper to taste

Directions:

1. Cook pasta in boiling water until cooked al dente.
2. Drain pasta.
3. Combine tomatoes, basil, and olive oil, and toss well.
4. Add sea salt and pepper.

Variations:

1. Serve with Nancy's Sensational Sea Salt Seasoning sprinkled on top.
2. Sprinkle with Parmesan cheese.

Notes:

1. Whole-wheat fusilli is a good choice for this recipe, as is gluten-free angel hair pasta by DeBoles.

2. I (Nancy) suggest serving this with whole-grain crusty bread.

3. My (Maryann's) ancestors came from Italy, and they would roll over in their graves if we served bread with pasta!

vegetarian/vegan/gluten-free

PEPPER PIE

I (Maryann) made this for my Dad. I didn't tell him it was a gluten-free pizza crust. His mom made pepper pie and it was his favorite pizza. When I served him mine, he said, "Wow! That's a blast from the past."

Ingredients:

- 4 red or green peppers, sliced in thin strips
- 3 T. pure olive oil
- 3 cloves garlic, minced
- 1 Gluten-Free Pizza Dough (see recipe on page 265)

Directions:

1. Sauté peppers in olive oil and garlic until tender. (Don't burn the peppers! This takes attention and time.)
2. Bake pizza dough according to recipe directions.
3. Remove pizza from oven and put cooked peppers on top.
4. Bake in oven for 15 minutes, or until brown, at 425 degrees F.

Note: I (Maryann) use scissors to cut the pizza.

Serving size: 2 servings

vegetarian/gluten-free (if using gluten-free linguini)

PESTO WITH LINGUINI

Ingredients:

1 c. fresh basil, washed and drained

½ tsp. unrefined sea salt

4 T. walnuts, chopped

¼ c. extra-virgin olive oil

¼ c. Parmesan cheese, grated

1 lb. whole-grain, organic linguini

Directions:

1. Set aside a few basil leaves, walnuts, and Parmesan for a garnish.

2. Combine basil, sea salt, walnuts, olive oil, and Parmesan in a food processor or blender, and pulse until smooth.

3. Cook linguini according to the package directions.

4. Drain linguini.

5. Transfer linguini to a bowl.

6. Toss linguini with pesto.

7. Place linguini on plates or in serving dish, and garnish with reserved basil, walnuts, and Parmesan cheese.

Variation: Substitute pine nuts for walnuts.

Serving size: 4 servings

vegetarian/vegan/ gluten-free

RICE AND WILTED LETTUCE

This is an easy recipe to make when you have leftover rice.

Ingredients:

¼ c. onion, chopped

2 T. extra-virgin, pure, organic coconut oil

1 tsp. sea salt

1 clove garlic, minced

3 c. whole-grain brown rice (cooked)

1 T. water

1 head romaine lettuce (cut into ½-inch strips)

Directions:

1. Sauté onions in coconut oil (or extra virgin olive oil) for a few minutes, until the onions are translucent.

2. Add the salt, garlic, and rice. Sauté for a couple of minutes.

3. Add the water, and then quickly add the romaine lettuce strips.

4. Sauté the mixture with the lettuce until it is just wilted and bright green, about 1 minute.

5. Remove from heat quickly and serve warm.

Variation: Substitute kale or Swiss chard for lettuce.

Serving size: 2 servings

Vegetables and Side Dishes

vegetarian/gluten-free

BAKED ACORN SQUASH

Ingredients:

- 2 acorn squash
- 3 T. ghee, melted, or melted butter
- 3 T. pure, extra-virgin, organic coconut oil, melted
- 4 T. honey or maple syrup
- 1 tsp. cinnamon
- 3 T. dried cranberries or raisins
- 4 T. pecans or walnuts, chopped
- Unrefined sea salt to taste
- Pepper to taste

Directions:

1. Preheat the oven to 375 degrees F.
2. Wash and dry squash. Cut in half, and remove seeds and fibers from inside. (Slice off just enough of the round backside of the squash for the squash to sit solidly when placed on a flat surface.)
3. Combine melted butter and coconut oil.
4. Mix together butter and oil mixture, honey, cinnamon, cranberries, chopped pecans, and a little salt and pepper in a small bowl.
5. Place squash in a large baking dish, cut side up. Put about ¼ inch of water in the

bottom of the baking dish.

6. Put equal amounts of the butter mixture in each squash.

7. Bake approximately 45–60 minutes. When you can pierce the meat of the squash with a fork and it's tender, the squash is ready.

8. Serve warm.

Note: Water creates a moist cooking environment so squash won't dry out or burn.

Serving size: 4 servings

vegetarian/vegan/gluten-free

BEANS

Start the recipe the day before you cook it. Soaking the beans makes them easier to cook. Beans are also more digestible when they are soaked overnight and the water is poured off.

Ingredients:

1 lb. dried beans (any variety)

10 c. water, plus more for soaking and cooking

2 T. pure, organic, extra-virgin coconut oil (optional)

2-inch piece kombu seaweed (optional)

Unrefined sea salt to taste

Directions:

1. Check beans: Discard any shriveled or discolored beans, and check to make sure there are no little stones or foreign matter mixed in.

2. Soak beans overnight in water. Make sure the dish is large enough for beans to double in size and that there's enough water to cover beans by at least 2 inches. Add kombu seaweed to the water at this time, if using.

3. Pour off water.

4. In a 5-quart saucepan, bring 10 c. fresh water and beans to a boil.

5. Discard water and keep beans.

6. Refill pot with new purified water to about 2 inches over the top of the beans.

7. Bring water and beans to a boil again.

8. Reduce heat to a simmer, add coconut oil, and cook beans until tender, about 45–60 minutes, depending on the size of beans. (Larger beans will take longer.) Add more water if it gets too low and the tops of beans are showing.

9. Add sea salt to taste, if using.

Notes:

1. One pound of dried beans will yield about 5 or 6 cups of cooked beans.

2. Seaweed adds nutrients and helps make the beans more digestible.

3. Add salt, if using, only after cooking. Salt can make beans tough.

4. Beans are high in fiber, protein, and flavor. Store uncooked, raw beans in a dark, cool, dry place. Cooked beans are easy to freeze and thaw later; make a large batch and freeze them to use later. Add beans to salads or as a side dish with soup or bread.

Serving size: 8 servings

vegetarian/vegan/gluten-free

BEETS

Ingredients:

1 lb. beets
3 T. extra-virgin olive oil
Sea salt to taste
Pepper to taste
3 garlic cloves, minced
½ c. goat cheese, crumbled
Handful of walnuts

Directions:

1. Boil, peel, and chop beets.
2. Drizzle beets with olive oil, salt, and pepper, and top with goat cheese and walnuts.
3. Serve warm.

Serving size: 4 servings

vegetarian/gluten-free

BROILED TOMATOES

Ingredients:
4 medium tomatoes
Unrefined sea salt to taste
Pepper to taste
4 large slices mozzarella cheese

Directions:
1. Cut off the top of each tomato.
2. Cut off a small part of the bottom of each tomato (so it sits steady in a pan).
3. Season tomatoes with salt and pepper to taste.
4. Place mozzarella cheese slice on top of each tomato.
5. Broil tomatoes until the cheese has just melted.
6. Serve warm.

Serving size: 4 servings

vegetarian/gluten-free

EASY SPAGHETTI SQUASH

Ingredients:

1 spaghetti squash

4 T. butter or extra-virgin olive oil

3 T. organic feta cheese

Unrefined sea salt to taste

Pepper to taste

Directions:

1. Pierce the outer shell of squash with a fork a few times.

2. Bake whole at 400 degrees F until tender (approximately one hour).

3. Remove from heat and let cool a few minutes.

4. Cut squash in half and "string" squash with the tines of a fork.

5. Add butter or extra-virgin olive oil.

6. Add crumbled feta cheese on top.

7. Season with salt and pepper to taste.

Note: This squash has Vitamin A, loads of Vitamin C, potassium, fiber, and manganese.

Serving size: 2 servings

vegetarian/gluten-free

GRAINS

Millet, quinoa, and amaranth are alkaline and easy to digest. Soak grains for a few hours before cooking.

Ingredients:

1 c. millet, quinoa or amaranth

2 c. water*

*Increase water to 3 c. if using amaranth.

Directions:

1. Put millet, quinoa, or amaranth in a saucepan with water, and bring to a boil.
2. Lower heat, cover pot, and cook about 20 minutes. (Make sure it doesn't burn.)
3. Serve warm.

Note: Amaranth contains more protein than any other gluten-free grain. Amaranth also contains amounts of Vitamin E in similar amounts to olive oil. The word "amaranth" means everlasting in Greek.

Serving size: 2 servings

vegetarian/vegan/gluten-free/raw

GRATED ZUCCHINI

Ingredients:

2 zucchini (raw)

1–2 T. extra-virgin olive oil

Unrefined sea salt to taste

Directions:

1. Grate zucchini, making short thin strips.

2. Make a mound of zucchini, and drizzle with olive oil and sea salt.

Notes:

1. When grating the zucchini, don't grate the zucchini down to the seeds.

2. I (Maryann) made this for Nancy once when she came to visit me once in New York City. You would have thought I invented sliced bread. She loved it so much, we decided to put it in our book.

Serving size: 2 servings

vegetarian/vegan/gluten-free

GRILLED ZUCCHINI

Ingredients:
1½ lb. zucchini (about 5 medium)
¼ c. pure, olive oil
Juice of 1 lemon (optional)
Sea salt to taste

Directions:
1. Trim ends of zucchini, and slice each lengthwise just under ¼ inch thick.
2. In a large, shallow dish, combine zucchini slices with oil, coating slices well.
3. Place a large ridged griddle or ridged cast-iron skillet over medium-high heat.
4. When griddle is hot, add zucchini slices in a single layer.
5. Cook, turning frequently, until slices are soft and scorched with a crisscross pattern of griddle marks.
6. Transfer to a large plate.
7. To serve, sprinkle with lemon juice, if using, and salt to taste.
8. Serve warm or room temperature.

Serving size: 4 servings

vegetarian/gluten-free

MARYANN'S MESQUITE BRUSSELS SPROUTS AND CARROTS

Brussels sprouts are one of my (Maryann's) father's favorite vegetables so I made them often for him. I cut vegetables into small pieces, making them easier for my father to eat.

Ingredients:

1 lb. Brussels sprouts, washed and cut in half

3 carrots, sliced in ¼-inch-thick rounds

1 clove garlic, chopped

4 T. extra virgin organic olive oil or extra-virgin, organic coconut oil

Mesquite spice to taste

Unrefined sea salt to taste

Pepper to taste

Directions:

1. Steam Brussels sprouts and carrots until tender.
2. Sauté garlic in olive or coconut oil until tender.
3. Add Brussels sprouts and carrots to oil and sauté for a few minutes.
4. Add mesquite (a pinch) to taste.
5. Add a pinch of sea salt and pepper
6. Sauté for a few more minutes.

Serving size: 2 servings

vegetarian/gluten-free

ROASTED BROCCOLI

Ingredients:

1½ T. pure olive oil

4 cloves garlic, minced

2 c. broccoli, cut into small florets

2 T. Parmesan cheese (optional)

Unrefined sea salt to taste

Pepper to taste

2 T. pine nuts or walnuts, toasted (optional)

Directions:

1. Preheat the oven to 425 degrees F.
2. Combine olive oil and garlic.
3. Coat broccoli with olive oil/garlic mixture.
4. Place broccoli in a roasting pan.
5. Roast broccoli 5–8 minutes. (Do not let it get brown.) Toss halfway through so it cooks evenly.
6. Remove from oven and grate Parmesan, if using, on top.
7. Sprinkle with sea salt and pepper.
8. Toss with toasted pine nuts or walnuts, if using.

Serving size: 4 servings

vegetarian/vegan/gluten-free

ROASTED BRUSSELS SPROUTS

Ingredients:

1 lb. Brussels sprouts, washed and cut in half

2 T. extra virgin organic olive oil or pure, extra-virgin, organic coconut oil

Sea salt to taste

Pepper to taste

Directions:

1. Toss Brussels sprouts with oil, salt, and pepper.
2. Roast at 450 degrees F until crispy, about 30–40 minutes.

Notes:

1. The roasting method mellows any bitterness in the sprouts.
2. This was one of Larry Hagman's favorite dishes that I (Nancy) made for him when I was his chef.
3. I (Maryann) taught my nephew Dean how to make this recipe. It is now one of his favorites.

Serving size: 2 servings

vegetarian/gluten-free

ROASTED ROOT VEGETABLES

Ingredients:

1 sweet potato

2 parsnips

2 carrots

2 turnips

organic olive oil

Unrefined sea salt to taste

Pepper to taste

Rosemary, thyme, or sage, fresh if possible

Directions:

1. Preheat the oven to 375 degrees F.
2. Wash and chop all vegetables into large bite-sized pieces.
3. Place vegetables in a large baking dish with sides.
4. Drizzle with olive oil; mix well to coat each vegetable lightly with oil.
5. Sprinkle with salt, pepper, and herb(s).
6. Bake uncovered 25–35 minutes, until vegetables are tender and golden brown, checking every 10 minutes to stir and make sure vegetables are not sticking.

Variation: Substitute extra-virgin coconut oil for olive oil.

Notes:

1. Any combination of vegetables will work. Roasting only one kind of vegetable also makes a nice side dish.

2. Nancy and I (Maryann) do not peel our vegetables. For years our families thought we were weird. A great amount of the nutrients are in the peel. We do clean our vegetables extremely well.

Serving size: 4–6 servings

vegetarian/gluten-free

SAUTÉED ASPARAGUS

Ingredients:

2 lb. asparagus

1 T. pure, extra-virgin, organic coconut oil

2 T. ghee

2 T. lemon juice

Sea salt to taste

Pepper to taste

½ c. slivered almonds (optional)

½ c. organic Parmesan cheese (optional)

Directions:

1. Rinse asparagus and trim off the thick, harder ends. Cut each asparagus stalk into two or three bite-sized pieces.

2. Sauté asparagus and coconut oil in a skillet for about 5 minutes, or until asparagus becomes a bright green and is warm.

3. Transfer asparagus from a skillet to a serving dish.

4. In the same skillet, melt ghee and combine it with lemon juice.

5. Drizzle ghee/lemon juice mixture over asparagus.

6. Sprinkle with salt and pepper.

7. Sprinkle with almonds and Parmesan cheese, if using.

8. Serve warm.

Serving size: 4–6 servings

vegetarian/vegan/gluten-free

SAUTÉED ESCAROLE

Grandma De Leo lived with my (Maryann's) cousin Roni and her family in Brooklyn. Roni told me that my grandmother cooked greens every night and served them as the first course for dinner. She made either chicory, spinach, escarole, Swiss chard, or kale.

Ingredients:

2 garlic cloves, minced

3 tsp. extra virgin organic olive oil

1 carrot, diced

1 head escarole, washed, drained, and torn into small pieces

Directions:

1. Sauté garlic in olive oil. (Don't let the garlic brown.)

2. Add diced carrots and sauté until they are tender.

3. Add escarole and cook until it is wilted.

Variation: Substitute spinach or kale for escarole. (Any green will work.)

Notes:

1. Add pasta, quinoa, or rice to escarole, or serve alone.

2. Greens can be very sandy, so be certain to wash them well.

Serving size: 2 servings

vegetarian/vegan/gluten-free

SAUTÉED KALE

Ingredients:

1 medium-sized bunch of kale

extra virgin organic olive oil (enough to cover the sauté pan and sautéed the garlic)

3 cloves garlic, chopped.

Sea salt to taste

Directions:

1. Wash kale well. Rinse a few times.
2. Heat olive oil over moderate heat. Add garlic and sauté for a few minutes. (Don't let the garlic brown.)
3. Add kale and sauté 5–10 minutes, depending on how crunchy you like it.
4. Add a little sea salt.

Notes:

1. Wrap kale in a towel or use a salad spinner to get the excess water out after washing.
2. Chop kale into small pieces with the stems, or tear the leaves from the stems and chop or rip those into small pieces.
3. I (Maryann) serve this with crusty Italian bread; that's how we ate it at my house. Dip the bread in the dish and let it soak up the olive oil. Toast the bread to make it crustier.

Variations:
1. Add crushed red pepper for a little heat.
2. Substitute coconut oil for olive oil.

Serving size: 2 servings

vegetarian/gluten-free

SAUTÉED SWISS CHARD

Raw Swiss chard has only 7 calories per cup, and it's delicious! Eat this alone or add it to pasta.

Ingredients:

1 bunch Swiss chard, washed well and
    chopped into bite-sized pieces

3 T. high-heat olive oil or pure, extra-virgin,
    organic coconut oil

Unrefined sea salt to taste

Directions:

1. Sauté Swiss chard lightly in oil.

2. Add sea salt to taste.

Serving size: 2 servings

vegetarian/vegan/gluten-free

SHISHITO PEPPER SAUTÉ

Chef Joseph Nieves, from the fabulous EATALY on Fifth Avenue in New York City, contributed this recipe. EATALY is a gourmet heaven with four restaurants, a bakery, a grocery store, and more. The shishito pepper is not hot, but light and deliciously flavorful, and full of nutrients. This dish is easy and delicious!

Ingredients:

1 c. whole, fresh shishito peppers

Splash of fresh lemon juice

Sea salt to taste

Directions:

1. Pan-fry peppers over a high heat with lemon juice and a sprinkle of sea salt for 1 minute.

2. Remove from heat and serve.

Serving size: 4 servings

vegetarian/vegan/gluten-free

STEAMED ARTICHOKES

My (Nancy's) family always serves melted butter or a hollandaise sauce with the artichokes. We use that as the dip for the ends of the leaves and the heart of the artichoke.

Ingredients:
4 large artichokes
2 garlic cloves
1 c. hot water
3 tsp. unrefined sea salt

Directions:
1. Remove outer leaves of artichokes.
2. Clip remaining leaf ends and wash well.
3. Cut off stems.
4. Peel garlic and cut each clove in two lengthwise.
5. Put one garlic piece among the leaves of each artichoke.
6. Stand artichokes in a saucepan into which they fit snuggly and that has a tight fitting cover.
7. Mix hot water, salt, and oil, stirring until salt is dissolved.
8. Pour hot water mixture over artichokes, so

oil and salt are evenly distributed among the leaves.

9. Cover with a tight lid and cook over low heat for 1 hour or until leaves are thoroughly soft, like butter.

10. Serve warm.

Notes:

1. Melt butter and add lemon juice to use as a dipping sauce, if desired.

2. Watch the artichokes so that they do not cook dry. Add more water if necessary, but see that the water is never more than just covering the bottom of the pan. You want just enough water to provide steam. (Alternatively, you can put them in a steamer basket.)

3. Serve with a large bowl to put the used artichoke leaves into after eating. When you get down to the heart of the artichoke, use a spoon to scrape off the hair-like covering, then use the spoon to scoop out the heart to eat.

4. You can find easy to make hollandaise sauce mixes at the grocery store.

Serving size: 4 servings

vegetarian/gluten-free

SWEET POTATOES WITH CRANBERRIES AND APPLES

Ingredients:

3 sweet potatoes, cut into 1-inch chunks

6 T. butter or ghee

1 green sour apple, cored, and diced

1 c. raw cranberries

½ c. raisins

3 T. xylitol or raw unrefined sugar

½ c. orange juice

Directions:

1. Preheat the oven to 350 degrees F.
2. Use 3 T. of the butter to butter a large baking dish.
3. Place sweet potatoes in buttered baking dish.
4. Top with apples, cranberries, and raisins.
5. Sprinkle with sugar.
6. Pour orange juice over top. Place remaining 2 T. butter in little pieces on top.
7. Cover and bake for 1 hour and 15 minutes, or until sweet potatoes are tender when pierced with a fork.

Variations:

1. Add ¼ c. chopped pecans or walnuts.
2. Substitute dried cranberries for fresh.

3. Substitute maple syrup for the sugar.

Serving size: 6 servings

Soups

vegetarian/vegan (depending on the choice of broth)/gluten-free

BASIC SOUP RECIPE

Ingredients:

1 T. extra virgin organic olive oil or coconut oil

2–3 cloves garlic, chopped

1 onion, chopped

1 c. mushrooms, sliced

2 c. vegetable or chicken stock or broth

2 c. vegetables, chopped (a mixture)*

Fresh parsley (for garnish)

Unrefined sea salt to taste

Fresh parsley (to garnish)

*This will be your main ingredient. Choose something that will puree nicely: potatoes, sweet potatoes, carrots, winter squash, peas, roasted peppers, canned or pre-cooked beans, or even roasted eggplant.

Directions:

1. Heat oil over medium-high heat.
2. Sauté garlic, onion, and mushrooms.
3. Add stock and bring to a simmer.
4. Add vegetable(s).
5. Reduce heat to medium, cover, and simmer until vegetables are tender.

6. Uncover, remove from heat, and puree, adding a little more stock if necessary.

7. Add sea salt and heat through over low heat.

8. Garnish with fresh parsley.

Note: You can put soup in a blender to puree, but don't use a food processor. When you use a blender, put the top on tightly. If it's hot, be careful; it can expand, push the top of the blender off, and make a mess. Blend only half of the soup at a time. Put a towel over the tightly closed lid, and hold it down when you turn it on. Be careful not to burn yourself with the hot soup.

Variations:

1. Add some whole-grain, cooked penne or small-shell pasta to make this more filling and heartier. Do not use any white refined or enriched pasta.

2. Use one boullion cube for one cup of water rather than broth.

Serving size: 4 servings

vegetarian (depending on choice of broth)/ gluten-free (depending on croutons)

BUTTERNUT SQUASH SOUP

This is a variation of my (Nancy's) mother's soup recipe.

Ingredients:

1 (2½ lb.) butternut squash

Unrefined sea salt to taste

Pepper to taste

4 cloves garlic, minced

Water

1 medium onion, diced

5 T. butter

2½ c. vegetable or chicken broth

1 c. organic milk

Dollop of sour cream as a topping (optional; this makes a pretty presentation)

Directions:

1. Preheat the oven to 400 degrees F.
2. Cut squash in half lengthwise and scoop out the seeds.
3. Season the flesh with salt and pepper.
4. Place garlic cloves in the squash cavities. Place squash halves, skin-side down, in a baking dish.
5. Pour in enough water to come ¾ inch up

the side of the dish. Bake 1 hour, or until flesh is soft.

6. Remove garlic. Reserve 2 roasted garlic cloves.
7. Scoop out squash pulp and mash with reserved roasted garlic cloves.
8. In a soup pot, sauté onion in butter until softened and beginning to brown around the edges.
9. Add broth and mashed squash.
10. Stir to combine thoroughly. Simmer mixture, uncovered, 10 minutes.
11. Puree in a blender or food processor in batches.
12. Return soup to pot and add milk of choice to thin soup to a creamy consistency.
13. Season with salt and pepper to taste.
14. Top each serving with a dollop of sour cream, if using.

Variations:

1. If you don't want to use sour cream but want a pretty presentation, use a sprinkle of fresh chopped pecans or walnuts, or some whole-grain croutons.
2. Substitute white pepper for black pepper.

Note: Be very careful blending hot soup in a blender.

Just do small amounts at a time. Make sure to cover the lid well, and put a cloth kitchen towel over the top, just to make sure it doesn't build up pressure and explode, or escape, when blending.

Serving size: 6 servings

vegetarian/gluten-free

ITALIAN ONION SOUP

When I (Maryann) made this for my parents, my dad said it was delicious. My mom said it had too many onions!

Ingredients:

2 T. extra virgin organic olive oil
1 T. garlic, minced
8 c. sweet onions, thinly sliced
Sea salt to taste
1 T. fresh sage, finely chopped
¼ c. balsamic vinegar
4 c. vegetable or chicken stock
Whole-grain croutons or slices of whole-grain toast
2 c. Gruyere or Fontina cheese for topping

Directions:

1. Heat olive oil in a large skillet over medium heat.
2. Add garlic and sauté for a few moments. (Do not let brown.)
3. Add onions and a little salt.
4. Sauté, stirring often, about 5 minutes.
5. Reduce heat and cook, stirring occasionally, until the onions are golden brown, 10–15 minutes.

6. Add sage and balsamic vinegar, and cook until the liquid evaporates.
7. Add stock and simmer about 5 minutes.
8. Bring to a boil.
9. Preheat the broiler.
10. Transfer soup to an oven-safe bowl or individual -sized oven-safe bowls.
11. Top with whole-grain croutons, then with cheese. (If the soup is in individual dishes, use about ½ cup cheese per dish.)
12. Place in the broiler.
13. Broil or bake until cheese melts.
14. Serve warm.

Serving size: 4 servings

vegetarian/gluten-free

NANCY'S NUTRITIOUS BROTH

This is a great broth, especially for someone who isn't feeling well. I (Nancy) drain off the vegetables and drink the broth. You can save the vegetables and eat them, or eat it all together as a vegetable soup.

This is a very alkalizing meal.

Ingredients:

1 zucchini

4 carrots

2 celery stalks

1 large potato (preferably purple, yam, or
     sweet potato)

½ onion

5 c. pure water

1 clove garlic, minced (optional)

Sea salt to taste

Pepper to taste

Directions:

1. Cut vegetables into chunks.
2. Place vegetable chunks in a large pot with water.
3. Bring to a boil.
4. Cook until potatoes are tender.

5. Add garlic, if using, at the end for a few minutes to simmer.

6. Strain off vegetables and drink broth.

Variation: Substitute frozen vegetables for fresh.

Note: Garlic is fragile. Don't cook it too long. You want it to retain as much of its nutritional value as possible.

Serving size: 6 servings

vegetarian/gluten-free

PROVENCAL SPINACH AND POTATO SOUP

Ingredients:

5 c. water, vegetable stock, or garlic broth

5 large garlic cloves, minced and pressed

2 T. extra virgin organic olive oil

5 medium potatoes, sliced (new, russet, purple, Yukon gold, or sweet)

½ tsp. parsley

¼ tsp. thyme

1 bay leaf

2 lb. spinach, stems removed, and leaves washed and chopped

Unrefined sea salt to taste

Pepper to taste

Whole-grain garlic croutons (optional)

4 medium eggs

To serve on the side:

Whole-grain crusty bread

Dipping Oil (extra-virgin olive oil, some freshly ground black pepper, and a dash of balsamic vinegar)

Directions:

1. Combine water or stock, garlic, olive oil, potatoes, parsley, thyme, and bay leaf in a large soup pot or casserole dish that can be put on the stovetop, and bring to a boil.

2. Reduce heat, cover, and simmer 30 minutes.
3. Remove bay leaf.
4. Stir in spinach, sea salt, and freshly ground pepper.
5. Taste and adjust the seasonings.
6. Reduce the heat to a bare simmer.
7. Add some garlic croutons, if using, into each serving bowl and set aside.
8. Carefully break eggs into the soup. Cook until they are set, about 6–8 minutes.
9. When eggs are almost cooked (meaning the yellow is still soft), gently ladle the soup with an egg on top into each bowl.
10. Serve immediately with crusty, whole-grain bread and accompaniments.

Note: You can make broth using one bouillion cube for each cup of water.

Variation: Substitute sage for thyme.

Serving size: 4 servings

vegetarian/vegan/gluten-free/raw

RAW GREEN SOUP

Ingredients:

1 bunch kale, chopped

½ c. parsley, chopped

1½ c. lettuce (romaine, red leaf, or spring mix)

½ c. spinach

1 T. extra-virgin organic olive oil or walnut oil

Unrefined sea salt to taste

Pepper to taste

1–2 c. water

Directions:

1. Blend kale, parsley, lettuce, spinach, oil, and water in a blender until smooth.

2. Add water a little at a time until the soup is the right consistency.

Serving size: 4 servings

vegetarian/vegan/gluten-free/raw

REFRESHING SUMMER SOUP

This is a fresh and living (raw) green soup.

Ingredients:

½ cucumber, chopped

1½ c. fresh green beans

½ c. romaine lettuce

½ c. fresh spinach

½ c. fresh basil

¼ c. fresh chives

1T. pure, organic, extra-virgin coconut oil

½ tsp. unrefined sea salt

1 T. fresh lime juice

1 T. fresh chives (for garnish)

Directions:

1. Place all ingredients except the chives for garnish in a powerful blender or food processor and blend.
2. Garnish with chives.

Serving size: 4 servings

Salads

vegetarian/vegan/gluten-free/raw

AVOCADO SALAD

Ingredients:

- 2 oranges or tangerines
- 2 avocados
- 4 very thin slices of onion (red is preferable)
- 3 T. extra-virgin olive oil
- 1 tsp. mint (fresh), chopped
- 1 T. freshly squeezed lime juice (about half of a small lime)
- ¼–½ tsp. Sensational Sea Salt Seasoning
- 1/8 tsp. fresh ground pepper

Directions:

1. Peel oranges with a knife, removing all of the white pith, and cut crosswise into thin wheels.
2. Pit, peel, and slice avocados, and put in a medium bowl.
3. Add oranges, onions, olive oil, mint, lime juice, sea salt seasoning, and pepper, and mix well.

Variation: Substitute unrefined sea salt for Sensational Sea Salt Seasoning.

Note: The Sensational Sea Salt Seasoning is included in the Resources.

Serving size: 4 servings

vegetarian/gluten-free/raw

FANCY TOMATO SALAD

Serve this salad at room temperature or cold on a hot summer day.

Salad Ingredients:
    1 cucumber, sliced
    1 red or yellow bell pepper, sliced
    1 small–medium onion (sweet, Vidalia, or red), sliced
    3 large tomatoes, sliced

Dressing Ingredients:
    3 T. balsamic vinegar
    3 T. extra-virgin organic olive oil
    1 T. honey (optional)
    1 T. fresh basil, chopped (or ½ tsp. dried)
    ¼ tsp. sea salt

Directions:
1. Combine all dressing ingredients and set aside.
2. Combine all salad ingredients and toss in a bowl.
3. Add dressing to salad and toss.

Note: When slicing the vegetables, the bell pepper looks pretty when it is sliced so that it retains it pretty shape all around the middle instead of just slicing it lengthwise strips. The onions look really pretty sliced into rings. The tomatoes can be made into chunks.

Serving size: 2 servings

vegetarian/vegan/gluten-free/raw

GREEN SALAD

Salad Ingredients:

2 heads romaine lettuce

½ cucumber

2 celery ribs

2 T. fresh sprouts (sunflower are a great choice)

Dressing Ingredients:

3 T. extra-virgin organic olive oil

1½ T. lemon juice

1 tsp. honey

1 tsp. Dijon mustard

½ tsp. sea salt

¼ tsp. freshly ground pepper

Directions:

1. Tear romaine into bite-sized pieces and put in a salad bowl.
2. Halve cucumber lengthwise, spoon out the seeds, and slice thinly on a diagonal.
3. Slice celery into small, ¼-inch to ½-inch slices.
4. Add cucumber, celery, and sprouts to the bowl containing the romaine.
5. Whisk together all dressing ingredients in a small bowl until emulsified.
6. Add dressing to salad, and toss to coat.

Variation: Add some other greens to this salad. Spinach, kale, watercress, and red leaf lettuce all work well in this salad. Each green will provide a different array of nutrients to the salad.

Note: Romaine can be washed and dried one day ahead, and then wrapped in dampened paper towels in a sealed bag.

Serving size: 6 servings

vegetarian/vegan/gluten-free

PEAS AND CORN SALAD

I (Nancy) don't know when, but I started putting barbecue sauce in many of my bean recipes years ago. It gives the beans a sweet flavor. I think it must be a Texas or Southern thing I picked up along the way. I also like combining beans and peas in recipes. I like the higher protein content, but it is also more interesting in flavor.

This can be served as a main dish served with corn bread. I serve this on New Year's Day, because it has black-eyed peas in it. In the South, black-eyed peas are eaten for good luck. Make it at least a day ahead of time, so it can marinate.

Serve this salad with whole-grain, organic cornbread, whole-grain focaccia, whole-grain pita bread, or corn chips.

Ingredients:

1½ c. black-eyed peas (cooked)

1½ c. English, green peas (cooked)

1½ c. corn (raw or cooked)

½ c. red bell pepper, seeded and chopped

1 c. red or sweet onion, finely chopped

2 T. balsamic vinegar

1½ T. extra virgin, pure, organic coconut oil (melted)

¼ tsp. dried mustard

1 T. barbecue sauce

½ tsp. unrefined sea salt

½ tsp. freshly ground black pepper

¼ c. parsley (fresh), finely chopped

1 T. basil (fresh), finely chopped

Directions:

1. Mix all ingredients together well, except parsley and basil.
2. Refrigerate at least four hours or overnight.
3. Before serving, add parsley and basil.

Variation: Substitute ½ tsp. hot sauce plus 1 T. honey for the barbecue sauce.

Serving size: 6 servings

vegetarian/vegan/gluten-free/raw

RED CABBAGE SLAW

Serve this at room temperature, or refrigerate and serve chilled. Sometimes it tastes better after sitting overnight, when the flavors have blended together.

Ingredients:
1½ c. raisins
1 head cabbage
4 apples
2 carrots
2 T. apple cider vinegar
2 T. raw honey
Dash of sea salt

Directions:
1. Soak raisins in a little water to make them soft and plump.
2. Grate cabbage, apples, and carrots.
3. Combine all ingredients in a bowl.

Variation: Add a few tablespoons of mayonnaise for a richer, creamier dish.

Note: Use any kind of cabbage or apple for this recipe. Granny Smith is a nice choice for the apple.

Serving size: 6 servings

vegetarian/vegan/gluten-free/raw

SPINACH SALAD

Most people enjoy this salad. Even when my (Nancy's) son was a teenager and wasn't much of a salad fancier, he loved this salad. The tangerine slices have lots of Vitamin C, which help the body absorb the iron in the spinach more easily.

Ingredients:
1 bunch baby spinach (fresh)
1 c. raw almond slivers
2 tangerines or oranges peeled, seeded and sectioned
½ c. sprouts
Oil and vinegar, or poppy seed salad dressing

Directions:
1. Tear spinach into bite-sized pieces.
2. Combine spinach, almonds, tangerines, and sprouts.
3. Toss salad with oil and vinegar, or poppy seed dressing.

Variation: Top with additional sprouts for serving.

Serving size: 2 servings

vegetarian/vegan/gluten-free/raw

TRI-COLOR SALAD

Ingredients:

½ c. grape tomatoes

1 carrot, grated

1 zucchini, grated with the skin

1 T. extra-virgin organic olive oil

¼ tsp. unrefined sea salt

¼ tsp. apple cider vinegar or balsamic vinegar

Directions:

1. Cut small tomatoes in half.
2. Combine tomatoes, carrots, and zucchini in a bowl.
3. Combine olive oil, salt, and vinegar, and mix well.
4. Add olive oil mixture to vegetable mixture, and toss well.

Note: For added nutritional value, don't peel the vegetables.

Serving size: 2 servings

vegetarian/gluten-free
WALDORF SALAD

My father and I (Maryann) were watching *Fawlty Towers*, and there was an episode about the mishaps of serving a Waldorf salad. I got inspired to make one. I made it for him often, and my mother likes it too.

Ingredients:
2 red apples, diced
1 T. fresh lemon juice
½ c. walnuts, chopped
1 stalk celery, diced
½ c. raisins
1 T. mayonnaise
Pinch of sea salt

Directions:
1. Toss apples with lemon juice.
2. Combine apples, walnuts, celery, and raisins.
3. Add mayonnaise, and mix to combine.
4. Season with sea salt.

Variation: Substitute Greek yogurt for mayonnaise.

Notes:
1. Don't peel the apples. The skin contains lots of the nutrients.

2. Tossing the apple with lemon juice keeps the apple from turning brown.

Serving size: 2 servings

Snacks

vegetarian/vegan/gluten-free
CHESTNUTS
Chestnuts were always part of our (Maryann's) Italian Christmas dinners. Chestnuts were served after the main course, along with bowls of fresh fruit and bowls of nuts in their shells. We spent hours cracking nuts and eating them, peeling chestnuts and oranges, and eating persimmons, pears, apples, and tangerines. The meal continued for at least three hours—sometimes longer! Eating chestnuts reminds me of those holiday dinners.

Ingredients:
1 lb. Italian chestnuts

Directions:
1. With a knife, carefully put an "X" in each uncooked chestnut.
2. Bake at 400 degrees for approximately 20–30 minutes. Try one to make sure the chestnuts are cooked.
3. Wrap chestnuts in a clean dish towel for a few minutes to let the steam escape. (This makes it easier to peel open the chestnuts.)

Serving size: 4 servings

vegetarian/vegan/gluten-free

CHICKPEA SNACK

My (Maryann's) father's mother made this for him and his brothers and sisters when he was a boy. It was his favorite snack. Whenever I made this for my father, he always talked about his childhood.

It's a nutritious snack for older people, and it's easy to eat.

Ingredients:
1 (12-oz.) can chickpeas, drained and rinsed in cool water
2 T. extra virgin organic olive oil
Sea salt
Cayenne pepper (optional)

Directions:
1. Preheat the oven to 450 degrees F.
2. Blot chickpeas with a paper towel to dry them.
3. In a bowl, toss chickpeas with olive oil, and season to taste with salt and cayenne, if using.
4. Spread on a baking sheet and bake 30–40 minutes, until browned and crunchy. (Watch carefully the last few minutes to avoid burning.)

Note: I (Maryann) use my toaster oven to make these.

Serving size: 2 servings

vegetarian/gluten-free/raw

DATE NUT BALLS

Start this recipe the night before you want to serve it. It can be made quickly and kept easily in the refrigerator for about three days. This is a raw-food snack with live enzymes and nutrients.

There are many easy little nibbles that can be made by rolling together different chopped nuts and dried fruits, coconut, carob/coco, and spices, and serving on toothpicks. Use some of your favorite dried fruits and nuts. You could also use this as a dessert.

Ingredients:

1½ c. organic, pure coconut (fresh or dried), grated

1 c. dates, pitted and soaked in water for 10 minutes

½ c. dried apricots, soaked in water for 10 minutes

1 c. walnuts, chopped

½ tsp. cinnamon

¼ tsp. nutmeg

Directions:

1. Place ½ c. coconut, along with dates, apricots, walnuts, cinnamon, and nutmeg, in a food processor and lightly pulse it to a soft dough consistency.

2. Shape dough into teaspoon-sized balls.
3. Put remaining 1 c. coconut in a bowl.
4. Roll finished balls in coconut flakes for a nice finished look.

Variations:
1. Substitute pecans or almonds for walnuts. (If you use almonds, soak them in water for an hour or more to make them softer and easier to blend.)
2. Substitute figs for dates.
3. Substitute raisins for dates. Soak them and plump them up.

Notes:
1. I (Nancy) like dried fruit to be in small pieces when I use them.
2. Pulse the mixture in the food processor until it's creamier if that's your preference.
3. I (Nancy) like my nutmeg freshly grated.

Serving size: 8 servings

vegetarian/gluten-free

GOAT CHEESE SNACKS

One of our favorite appetizers on bread with soups or salads is fresh raw goat cheese or goat cheese feta bought at the local farmer's market. Most people digest goat milk products better than cow milk products.

I (Nancy) read about a Swedish model who ate this every morning for breakfast. After I heard that, my daughter and I started eating this, too. It's one of our favorite ways to have toast any time of the day. The quality of the goat cheese is important. The raw cheese will have natural probiotics in it, whereas the pasteurized version won't. The heat used during pasteurization destroys the live enzymes.

Look for local farmer's markets in your area.

Ingredients:
Goat cheese
Whole-grain crackers or bread (toasted)

Directions:
1. Spread goat cheese on crackers or bread.

Note: I (Nancy) like this best when it is slightly warm.

vegetarian/gluten-free

KALE CHIPS

Ingredients:

1 lb. kale, stems removed and leaves torn into pieces

¼ c. pure olive oil

2 garlic cloves, minced

Unrefined sea salt to taste

Locatelli cheese, grated (optional)

Directions:

1. Preheat the oven to 375 degrees.

2. In a bowl, toss kale leaves with all but a tablespoon of olive oil and half of the garlic.

3. Spread out kale leaves on two baking sheets, and roast in the upper and lower thirds of the oven about 15 minutes, until crisp.

4. Season with sea salt and put on a large plate.

5. Sprinkle with grated cheese. (optional)

Variation: Substitute other grated cheese for Locatelli cheese. I (Maryann) use Locatelli because it's a family favorite. My parents always debated whether Locatelli was a brand name or a region in Italy. I can't remember who was right.

Note: Be careful not to burn the kale.

Serving size: 4 servings

vegetarian/gluten-free/raw

NANCY'S FAVORITE GUACAMOLE

Ingredients:

5 ripe avocados, pitted and peeled

1/3 red onion, finely chopped

1 garlic clove, crushed and minced

2 large tomatoes, diced

1/3 c. fresh cilantro, finely chopped

1 green chili, finely chopped

3 T. fresh lemon or lime juice

Directions:

1. Mash avocados in a large bowl, leaving some small chunks.

2. Mix in remaining ingredients.

Variations:

1. For a little zestier dip, add a few chilies or, if you are really brave, add a few chopped jalapeños!

2. Top with grated Monterey Jack cheese.

Note: Serve with multi-grain tortilla chips. Blue corn is 20% higher in protein than white corn.

Serving size: 12 servings

Sauces

vegetarian/vegan/gluten-free

BARBECUE SAUCE

This is delicious on burgers, grilled tempeh, mushrooms, or grilled vegetables. Use this sauce for grilled sandwiches or brush it on grilled, broiled, or baked food.

I (Nancy) make it and freeze it in small containers so I can use it as needed. Whenever you are creating a dish and something is missing, think about whether you have added something sweet, salty, sour, or spicy. When a recipe has all these, it's more satisfying and makes for a more interesting dish.

Ingredients:

½ c. apple or pear juice

1¼ c. tomato puree

4 or 5 dates, pitted and soaked in water for about an hour

3 T. melted, extra-virgin coconut oil or olive oil

3–4 garlic cloves, minced

2 T. hot sauce

1 T. molasses

1 T. mustard

1 T. apple cider vinegar

1½ tsp. ground turmeric

½–1 tsp. unrefined, sea salt

1 dried chipotle chile pepper

Directions:
1. Place all ingredients in a blender or food processor and blend well.

Note: Store in a tight-lidded container in the refrigerator for about a week.

Serving size: 8 servings

Desserts

BAKED APPLES

Ingredients:

4 apples, cored

4 T. butter, room temperature

3 T. honey or maple syrup

1 tsp. cinnamon

¼ tsp. unrefined sea salt

2/3 c. walnuts, chopped

½ c. water

Directions:

1. Heat the oven to 350 degrees F.
2. Place whole apples in a baking dish that has a lid.
3. Combine butter, honey or maple syrup, cinnamon, sea salt, and 1/3 c. of the chopped walnuts.
4. Place equal amounts of butter mixture in each apple.
5. Pour about ½ c. water in the dish, and cover with the lid.
6. Bake 30 minutes.
7. Remove the lid, and bake another 10–15 minutes.
8. Let apples cool a little.
9. Drizzle with juice from baking dish and

serve in little bowls that can hold the juice.

10. Sprinkle remaining chopped walnuts over each apple.

Variations:

1. Substitute pecans for walnuts.

2. Substitute xylitol or stevia for honey. (Stevia is 30 times sweeter, so use only a tiny bit.)

3. Substitute coconut oil for the butter.

4. Drizzle melted dark chocolate on the apple after baking.

Serving size: 4 servings

vegetarian/gluten-free

BAKED PEACHES

Ingredients:

4 peaches, halved and pitted
4 T. butter, room temperature
3 T. maple syrup or xylitol sugar
1 tsp. cinnamon
¼ tsp. unrefined sea salt
2/3 c. walnuts, chopped
¼ c. water

Directions:

1. Heat the oven to 350 degrees F.
2. Place whole peaches in a baking dish that has a lid.
3. Combine butter, maple syrup or sugar, cinnamon, sea salt, and 1/3 c. of the chopped walnuts.
4. Place equal amounts of butter mixture in each peach.
5. Pour a little less than ¼ c. water in the dish, and cover with lid.
6. Bake 30 minutes.
7. Let peaches cool a little.
8. Drizzle with juice from baking dish and serve in little bowls that can hold the juice.
9. Sprinkle remaining chopped walnuts over each peach.

Serving size: 4 servings

vegetarian

BRIE AND CHOCOLATE SANDWICH

To make this easier for my (Maryann's) dad to eat, I cut it with scissors into small pieces. When I went to see if he liked it, there were hints of chocolate at the corners of his mouth and the plate was empty.

Ingredients:

2 slices bread, whole grain, baquette or sour dough

Sliced Brie cheese (enough to cover a piece of bread)

2 T. bittersweet chocolate chips

Directions:

1. Toast bread lightly in a pan. (No butter is necessary).
2. Place slices of Brie on one side of the bread.
3. Sprinkle chocolate chips on top.
4. Place the other bread slice on top, and place the sandwich in a pan.
5. Grill, pressing down and cooking until brown on both sides.

Note: Sourdough bread works best.

Serving size: 1 serving

vegetarian/gluten-free (if gluten-free flour is used)

CARROT CAKE

Ingredients:

3 c. carrots, grated

3/4 c. honey, maple syrup, or rice syrup

½ c. melted, extra virgin organic coconut oil

½ c. butter, melted

4 egg yolks

2 c. oat flour (labeled gluten-free on package)

1/12 tsp. baking powder

1 tsp. cinnamon

½ tsp. mace

½ tsp. sea salt

½ c. raisins

½ c. walnuts, chopped

4 egg whites, beaten stiff

Directions:

1. Oil two round cake pans, then dust with flour and set aside.

2. Mix carrots, honey, oil, melted butter, and egg yolks.

3. Let the mixture sit for 20 minutes.

4. Sift together flour, baking powder, cinnamon, mace, and sea salt.

5. Stir flour mixture into wet ingredients.

6. Add raisins and walnuts.

7. Fold stiff egg whites into batter.

8. Pour batter into oiled pans.

9. Bake at 350 degrees F 30 minutes or until a toothpick comes out clean.

10. Cool 15–20 minutes before removing from pans. (Do not frost until cake is cold.)

Frosting Ingredients:

4 oz. organic cream cheese

¼ c. honey or rice syrup

½ tsp. vanilla

Directions:

1. Mix all frosting ingredients together.

2. Spread on cooled cake.

Variation: Mix buckwheat, rice, and organic quinoa flour for a non-gluten flour mix.

Note: A Bundt pan can be used, but you need to bake it about 15 minutes longer, until the toothpick comes out clean.

Serving size: 8 servings

vegetarian/gluten-free
CHOCOLATE CHIP COOKIES

I (Maryann) made these for my nieces and nephew, and they are always asking me to make them again.

Ingredients:

1 c. pure, extra-virgin, organic coconut oil

6 T. unsweetened applesauce

2 T. pure vanilla extract

1¼ c. xylitol or raw sugar

2 c. organic garbanzo bean flour

1 tsp. baking soda

1 tsp. unrefined sea salt

1½ tsp. xanthan gum

1 c. bittersweet chocolate chips

Directions:

1. Preheat the oven to 325 degrees F. Line baking sheets with non-aluminum paper.

2. In a large bowl, mix oil, applesauce, vanilla, and sugar together well.

3. In a medium bowl, sift together flour, baking soda, sea salt, and xanthan gum.

4. Using a rubber spatula, slowly add dry ingredients to the wet mixture, and stir until a grainy dough is formed.

5. Fold in the chocolate chips until they are evenly distributed.

6. Using a teaspoon, scoop cookie dough onto the prepared baking pans. Space them about an inch apart. Using a fork, gently press cookies down slightly.

7. Bake cookies in the center rack for about 15 minutes. Check the bottom of a cookie to see if it is lightly brown. When the bottoms are lightly brown, they are ready.

8. Take cookies out of the oven and let cool for about 10 minutes, and then transfer each cookie to a cooking rack to cool completely.

9. Store the cookies in an airtight container at room temperature for up to three days.

vegetarian

FAR BRETON CUSTARD CAKE

This is a French custard-y cake that my (Maryann's) father liked. When I made this at Christmas, it looked so perfect that my brother said, in disbelief, "You made that?"

Ingredients:

3 large eggs

2 c. whole milk

½ c. raw sugar or xylitol

1/8 tsp. unrefined sea salt

¼ tsp. vanilla extract

5 T. unsalted butter, melted and cooled, plus more for pan

¾ c. whole-grain flour, plus more for pan

1 c. pitted prunes

¼ c. raisins

¼ c. water

1 c. hot tea (non-flavored tea)

Confectioners' sugar, for dusting

Directions:

1. Place eggs, milk, sugar, salt, vanilla, and melted butter in a blender or food processor and blend for 1 minute.

2. Add flour, and blend or pulse several times.

3. Pour batter into a pitcher, cover, and refrigerate for 3 hours (or preferably overnight).

4. Meanwhile, place prunes, raisins, and water in a small saucepan over medium heat. Cook until water is almost evaporated.

5. Turn off heat and, in a heatproof bowl, pour tea evenly over fruit.

6. Let cool to room temperature, cover, and set aside.

7. Place rack in center of the oven and preheat to 375 degrees F.

8. Butter an 8-inch round cake pan with 2-inch depth, and line the bottom with parchment paper.

9. Butter the paper and dust the pan with flour, tapping out any excess.

10. Place the pan on a baking sheet.

11. Remove batter from refrigerator and whisk to re-blend.

12. Forcefully tap the bottom of the pitcher on the counter to break any air bubbles.

13. Pour batter into the prepared pan.

14. Add fruit, evenly distributing it within the batter, and discard any remaining soaking liquid.

15. Bake until top of cake is puffed and brown, and a thin knife inserted into center comes out clean, 50–60 minutes.

16. Transfer the pan to a wire cooling rack and cool to room temperature.
17. To unmold, place a piece of parchment or wax paper over the wire cooling rack and dust with confectioners' sugar.
18. Have your plate ready. Run a blunt knife between the cake and the sides of the pan, and gently turn cake out onto the prepared rack.
19. Quickly invert cake onto plate.

Variations (for a healthier version):
1. Substitute xylitol one for one with sugar.
2. Substitute rice milk or nut milk for whole milk.
3. Substitute ghee for butter, or use coconut oil and tiny bit of ghee instead.

Notes:
1. Maryann likes Earl grey tea in this recipe.

Serving size: 8 servings

vegetarian/gluten-free

FIGS WITH SHERRY

Serve over vanilla ice cream or vanilla coconut bliss.

Ingredients:

2 T. butter
1 tsp. xylitol or raw sugar
Pinch of sea salt
3 T. Spanish sherry
8 whole figs

Directions:

1. Combine butter, xylitol or raw sugar, and salt.
2. Add Spanish sherry in a skillet over medium heat.
3. Once mixture is lightly caramelized, add figs and toss to coat.
4. Cook until fruit softens.

Variation: Toss a pint of figs into an ovenproof dish and roast for about 10 minutes at 350 degrees F, then drizzle with balsamic vinegar.

Serving size: 4 servings

vegetarian/vegan/gluten-free/raw

RAW FOOD BROWNIE

Ingredients:

1½ c. walnuts, soaked at least 4 hours and rinsed very well

10 pitted dates

1¼ c. cacao powder for dark-chocolate brownies or 3/4 c. cacao

1 ground vanilla bean or 1 tsp. vanilla extract

Pinch of unrefined sea salt

Directions:

1. In a food processor pulse walnuts slightly to break them into smaller pieces.

2. Add remaining ingredients to food processor.

3. Process the mixture, adding very small amounts of water if necessary, until it starts to come together. Do not over-process. You want small chunks of walnut to remain. Do not add too much water, or you won't get a good batter.

4. Scoop the mixture into an 8×8 baking dish and press the mixture down firmly with the back of a heavy spoon.

5. Store in the refrigerator.

Note: I (Nancy) use Medjool dates.

vegetarian/gluten-free

SOAKED ORANGE SLICES

Serve this recipe chilled.

Ingredients:

6 oranges

¼ tsp. lemon peel, grated without digging into the white pith

5 T. sugar (xylitol, stevia, or raw sugar)

Juice of half a lemon

Directions:

1. Using a sharp paring knife, peel 4 of the 6 oranges, stripping away all the white, spongy pith and as much of the thin skin beneath it as possible.

2. Cut peeled oranges into slices less than ½-inch thick.

3. Remove all seeds from oranges.

4. Place orange slices on a deep platter or into a shallow serving dish.

5. Combine lemon peel and sugar, and sprinkle over the oranges.

6. Squeeze remaining 2 oranges, adding their juice to the platter or dish.

7. Add lemon juice and toss lightly.
8. Cover and refrigerate for at least four hours, or even overnight.
9. Toss gently after removing from refrigerator.

Variations:
1. Substitute 3 T. maple syrup or honey for sugar.
2. Garnish with a sprig of mint, if desired.

Note: Be careful cutting the oranges, the first time I (Maryann) made it, my mother asked, "Are the oranges supposed to taste like garlic?" Make sure you use a separate cutting board for garlic.

Serving size: 4 servings

Easy and Healthy Sorbets

I t's easy to make fruit sorbet with a blender. Blend the fruit till it's creamy and add a little coconut water, water, or fruit juice to make it a bit thinner, or add another flavor to the creamy mixture. Vanilla beans can be scraped and added, or you could add vanilla or almond extract.

For a sorbet recipe of two to three servings, use a pound of fruit. To add a nut flavor to the sorbet, soak the nuts overnight and then add the nuts to the mixture. Cashews can make sorbet really creamy and rich.

For more nutritional impact or calories, add a teaspoon or two of raw coconut oil or coconut crème to the mixture. You can add a teaspoon or two of lecithin granules to the mixture as well, or a half-teaspoon of bee pollen. These would boost the nutritional impact of the sorbet without changing the flavor.

Here are a few recipes that you can use as guidelines for creating your own sorbet delights.

vegetarian/vegan/gluten-free/raw

CHERRY SORBET

Ingredients:

2 c. cherries

¼ packet or a few drops stevia (or 2 T. xylitol)

¼–½ c. water, coconut water, or fruit juice

Pinch of sea salt

Directions:

1. Place all ingredients in a blender.
2. Blend until creamy.
3. Place in a shallow pan.
4. Freeze until firm.

Variation:

1. Add ½ c. raw cashews that have been soaked overnight in 1 c. water.
2. Add a banana.

Serving size: 4 servings

vegetarian /vegan/gluten-free/raw

PEACH SORBET

Ingredients:

1 lb. peaches

1 c. ice cubes

¼–½ c. orange juice

Directions:

1. Peel, pit, and slice peaches.
2. Put peaches in blender with ice and orange juice. Blend until creamy. Add more orange juice until you get the right consistency.
3. Place the mixture in a shallow pan.
4. Place in the freezer until it is a hard, sorbet consistency.

Variation:

1. Substitute apricot nectar, or pineapple, mango, or another fruit juice for orange juice.
2. Add a banana.

Serving size: 4 servings

Breads

vegetarian

CORNBREAD

I'm (Nancy) from Texas, where cornbread is a favorite staple.

Buy certified organic cornmeal. Blue corn has 20 percent more protein than yellow corn.

Serve this cornbread with ghee or organic butter, and honey.

Ingredients:

5 T. extra-virgin, organic coconut oil

1 c. cornmeal

½ c. whole-grain flour

½ tsp. unrefined, sea salt

1 T. baking powder

½ tsp. baking soda

1½ c. whole milk

2 eggs, beaten

2 T. honey

Directions:

1. Preheat the oven to 450 degrees F.

2. Add coconut oil to a 9x9 pan until the oil melts (about 2–3 minutes). Remove 4 T. of the oil and set aside. Leave the remaining tablespoon of oil to coat the pan.

3. Combine all dry ingredients in a mixing bowl and sift together.

4. In another bowl, combine all wet ingredients.

5. Add reserved melted coconut oil to wet ingredients and mix.

6. Stir together wet and dry ingredients quickly. Don't over-mix; it is all right if there are some small lumps.

7. Pour batter into the greased pan and place quickly into the oven. Do not disturb the oven while the bread is cooking.

8. Bake about 30 minutes. (When the top is lightly brown, insert a toothpick. When the toothpick comes out clean, the cornbread is done.)

9. Remove from the oven and cool slightly before serving.

Variation: Substitute about ½ c. sour cream, buttermilk or yogurt for ½ c. milk, for a richer-flavored bread.

Note: Whole wheat, oat, and quinoa are all good choices for the flour.

Serving size: 8 servings

vegetarian/gluten-free
GLUTEN-FREE PIZZA DOUGH

Ingredients:

2 c. gluten-free flour

2 tsp. xanthan gum

2 tsp. baking powder

¼ tsp. unrefined, sea salt

1 tsp. raw, unrefined sugar or xylitol

2 T. extra virgin organic olive oil

1½ c. sparkling water

Directions:

1. Preheat the oven to 425 degrees F.
2. Mix dry ingrédients.
3. Add wet ingredients and combine
4. Pat onto a pizza pan or use a cookie sheet. (The dough is a little wet when you pat it onto the pan.)
5. Bake 20 minutes without any topping.
6. After 20 minutes, remove from oven and add desired toppings.
7. Cook 15 minutes more.

Serving size: dough for 1 pizza

Note: Suggested toppings: goat cheese, parmesan cheese, mozzarella cheese, sautéed vegetables, sautéed peppers, mushrooms, tomato sauce, grilled veggies

vegetarian/gluten-free (if using gluten free flour)

PUMPKIN BREAD

This bread is great served thinly sliced and warm with a little butter or cream cheese.

Ingredients:

extra-virgin, organic coconut oil for pan

1½ c. raw brown sugar

½ c. butter (melted)

1½ c. cooked pumpkin

2 eggs

½ tsp. ground nutmeg

½ tsp. ground cinnamon

¼ tsp. ground ginger

2 c. whole-grain flour

1 T. baking soda

¼ tsp. unrefined sea salt

1 c. raisins

½ c. chopped walnuts or pecans

¼ c. water

Directions:

1. Preheat the oven to 350 degrees F.
2. Oil a loaf pan (9x5x3) with coconut oil and line bottom with oiled parchment paper.
3. Combine sugar, butter, pumpkin, water, and eggs.
4. Mix well, and then make a well in the middle of the mixture.

5. Sift nutmeg, cinnamon, ginger, flour, baking soda, and sea salt into the well of the mixture.
6. Blend all ingredients.
7. Add raisins, nuts, and water to the mixture and blend.
8. Spoon the mixture into greased loaf pan.
9. Bake about 65–75 minutes. Do the toothpick test to see if the middle is done, the toothpick should come out clean.

Variations:
1. Substitute about ½ cup of xylitol for ½ cup of sugar.
2. Substitute applesauce, yogurt, or coconut oil for butter.

Note: Use oat flour or quinoa flour for a non-gluten version.

Serving size: 8 servings

The Manicotti Lesson

Nancy and I drove home to Manhattan just at Sunday dusk under a streaked sky of long, thin, grayish and deep pink clouds.

We had spent the afternoon with my mother cooking—or learning to cook.

We started out listening to an opera CD that my brother David made for my mother. The music was to accompany the manicotti making that was about to begin.

"It just felt right," my mother said. "Yesterday when I was making the pizza, to be listening to opera. Some of it was so sad. Even though I didn't understand the words, I was crying while I was standing at the stove."

Then my mother darted from the stove to her CD stash.

"I love the Beatles," she said. "Let's get rid of the opera."

After she ejected poor Maria Callas just in the middle of the heart-crushing Mio Bambino (my mother doubted it was Maria Callas, and since she is also a singer I should believe her), she put in the Beatles (or so she thought).

She turned up the volume too loud, just like my teenage nephew does when he wants me to hear the latest music he loves, and she started sliding back and forth on her kitchen floor. "All we are saying is give peace a chance," she sang.

I didn't have the heart to tell my mother it wasn't the Beatles, but an ex-Beatle, John Lennon, and his wife, Yoko Ono, with The Plastic Ono Band. I just couldn't do it. I couldn't burst her Beatles bubble.

She kept singing, her voice getting louder with each chorus, her fingers finding the volume control and turning it up each time they chanted "All we are saying is give peace a chance."

"I just love the Beatles," she said again.

I remembered another winter, when I was 16, when my hippie boyfriend and I went Christmas caroling in our little suburban town. When we got to the first door and were about to knock, he said, "What carol should we sing?"

"Let's sing "Give Peace a Chance," I said, completely taken with myself at that suggestion. The Vietnam War was still going on, and I knew my neighbors might have had a different opinion than my blue-eyed, bearded boyfriend and I.

Back to my mother in her newly painted, bright, and cheerful kitchen. The song continued. Nancy and I looked at each other with big smiles on our faces at my mother's glee at the song.

When the music changed, John Lennon and Yoko sang another song, but my mother didn't sing along. It was back to the lesson—the manicotti lesson we had come to learn.

The afternoon changed as the sun moved away from the yellow kitchen window.

My mother got serious, giving instructions (or orders) to Nancy and me. She's always right, so it's hard to do anything but obey. "Don't use that pan," she told me, when I started to butter my small Cuisinart frying pan.

I persisted. "Let me try," I said, but soon I had a ragged puddle of manicotti batter in the pan. The lesson continued more easily once I gave in to my mother's expertise.

While she cooked she told me a story I had never heard. Picking up the manicotti shell with two fingers, hot to the touch but not too hot for her, and placing it gingerly onto the plastic wrap layers of finished shells, she said, "You know, Grandma De Leo used to make the manicotti shells in boiling water. It was not easy and often they fell apart in the water. I saw this new method in a magazine and I told my mother-in-law about it." (My grandmother was a master self-taught cook.)

My mother said, "She listened to this new method and concluded it was worth a try. If it were me I probably wouldn't have tried it, but my mother-in-law had an open mind"—just like my father did; now I could see where he got it from.

By mid- afternoon my sister Dorothea had arrived to join us for dinner.

By 4:00 p.m. the manicotti were constructed. One demonstration by my mother of how to carefully place the three cheeses inside the shell was done, and Nancy and I were left to complete the task.

My mother had calculated by eye exactly how much ricotta cheese was needed to fill all 16 manicotti. I made the incorrect assumption as we were nearing the end that we would be short cheese and added some. My mother came over like a supervisor. "No, you don't need more. That was about right," she said, after looking at the cheese that remained.

As the last manicotti was stuffed, I saw that the amount remaining was just about the amount I had added!

My mother had been right.

As usual.

At 4:30 p.m. we were sitting down with the baked manicotti and a bottle of my mother's latest wine find, a California zinfandel called Dancing Bear. "French is better," I said.

"No, I don't want to give my money to the French. I'd rather give it to California," she said.

My mother had a broken wine opener, missing its most vital piece. My mother told my sister to try anyway. My sister got the opener in the cork but couldn't pull the cork out.

Nancy, a native Texan and petite, like a Dallas wrangler, planted her feet on the floor and released the cork. The sound of the pop and the force of the cork releasing sent Nancy back a step or two, and a small gush of red wine spilled onto the creamy, light floor.

My mom sat with her wine and her manicotti. She ate the first bite. "Good," she said. "It's good."

"The cheese could be a little more melted," she added to her initial thumbs-up.

We all ate silently. Nancy closed her eyes and put the first bite into her mouth. "Delicious," she said.

At our meal my mother told a story about an Italian cook and her daughter. On their television cooking show, the daughter had baked a cake. When it was time to cut it, she cut herself, my mother showed us with her hands, a large piece of cake. My mother was horrified that they would eat like that on TV, slathering their cake with whipped cream and pouring chocolate sauce over it.

"Dad didn't like her," I said. "He said she was what was called 'high Italian.'" ("High Italian" means snobby.)

"He was right," my mother said. "He was right, fortunately or unfortunately, about everything." She sighed, her head dropping down.

We went away, each of us in that moment, mourning him and loving him, speaking of him, knowing he was with us. Yet his physical absence was so hard to understand, accept, and live with, for all of us in our own way.

My mother and my sister and I went to our own grief then, mine like a silent, interior tornado starting at my planted feet and lifting all the way to my head,

I've stopped running from the tornado, remembering what my father taught me about how a ship must head into the waves and not try to avoid them: "Head into the waves, and you will survive," he told me. "Try to circumvent them and you will perish. Although it seems frightening to head into the storm, you must."

I let myself head into what felt like a tornado of grief, then it rushed away, and I returned to the assessment of our homemade family meal—a meal my father would have loved, cooked by two of his favorite women for our favorite man.

He was a lucky man, and we were lucky, too.

Family Favorites

These are recipes from our beloved family and friends.

Main Dishes

vegetarian/vegan

CARLOS'S GAZPACHO

Ingredients:

1 green pepper
3 ripe large tomatoes
1/3 c. extra-virgin, unrefined olive oil
1 garlic clove (minced)
1 small piece Italian bread
1 tsp. unrefined sea salt
Water, for thickness

Directions:

1. Combine all ingredients in a blender.
2. Add water for thickness.
3. Blend at high speed.

Serving size: 2 servings

DAVID'S TRADITIONAL VALENCIAN PAELLA

You need a Paella pan for this dish—very wide and with low sides. This was taught to me by a good friend in Valencia, Spain, cooking over an outdoor fire. ~ *David De Leo*

Ingredients:

Extra virgin organic olive oil (enough to cover the bottom of the paella pan)

1 lb. chicken legs and thighs, or rabbit, cleaned, patted dry, and lightly salted

1 c. large butter beans or white lima beans

1 c. fresh wide green beans

2 medium, ripe tomatoes, chopped

1 level tsp. sweet red paprika

1 level tsp. saffron

8 c. hot water or chicken broth

3 c. Spanish rice

Sea salt to taste

Directions:

1. Add olive oil to paella pan.
2. When oil is hot, add chicken or rabbit, and fry until lightly browned.
3. Add white and green beans, and cook together with the meat.
4. While cooking meat and beans, make a well

in the middle of the pan, add the chopped tomatoes, and cook them a bit.

5. Add paprika, and then saffron, stirring quickly, and immediately add hot water or broth until it is almost to top of edge of paella pan.

6. Cook about 20 minutes over high heat and taste for salt.

7. After 20 minutes, add rice, distributing evenly. Make sure the rice is completely covered with liquid.

8. Keep the flame fairly high to maintain boiling. It takes about 20 minutes for the paella rice to cook.

9. Remove from heat and let stand 10 minutes, covering the top with newspaper. The rice grains should be loose, not clumped together or mushy.

10. Serve pan right to the table.

Variation: Substitute canned tomatoes.

Notes:
1. Do not stir the rice once you have added it to the paella pan. Just rotate the pan to get it took cook evenly. All the water/broth should be absorbed when finished.

2. Spanish olive oil is best to use in this recipe.
3. In Spain Garrafon beans are used.
4. If using canned beans, rinse them thoroughly with water and strain.
5. Use the best organic chicken you can find for this recipe.

Serving size: 4–6 servings

DOTTY'S MANICOTTI

My (Maryann's) grandmother Antoinette De Leo was a master cook. My mother said she was a creative cook, never using recipes or measurements, and doing everything by hand and eye. My grandmother's method for making manicotti was to make the pasta shell and boil it in water. My mother saw a recipe in a book that used a different method, which made the shell like a crepe in a frying pan—a thin batter, cooked for a few minutes. My mother said my grandmother thought about this new method and told my mother she would try it. She tried it, she liked it, and this became her method. My mother was impressed that my grandmother was open to trying a new way and not tied to the old method. My mother is also a master cook, who doesn't use recipes. She spent an afternoon showing Nancy and me how to make manicotti. She showed us each step to perfecting the shell, mixing the ricotta with just the right amount of salt and pepper, grating the mozzarella, and how much grated cheese to sprinkle over the cheeses. This is my mother's recipe.

Pasta Ingredients:
3 eggs
Pinch of salt

1 c. milk

½ c. flour

Directions:

1. Beat eggs with an eggbeater.
2. Add a pinch of salt, and beat well. (Eggs should be frothy.)
3. Add milk a little at a time while beating.
4. Add flour a little at a time, and continue beating.
5. Heat a small amount of butter in a 6-inch frying pan.
6. Put approximately 2 large tablespoons of batter in pan, covering the bottom of pan. Swirl batter around so it covers pan.
7. Let cook about 1–3 minutes on one side. (It can be getting lightly brown.)
8. Carefully, with your fingers, turn shell over, and cook for a minute or two on the other side
9. Remove the pasta crepe from the pan.
10. Put cooked shells on a cooking sheet covered in plastic wrap or wax paper, with a layer of plastic wrap or wax paper between each layer.

Filling Ingredients:

2 c. ricotta cheese

½ c. fresh parsley, chopped finely
1 egg, beaten
¼ tsp. sea salt
¼ tsp. black pepper

Directions:

1. Combine ricotta, parsley, egg, salt, and pepper.

Directions to Assemble Manicotti:

1. Set filling aside until pasta is made.
2. Warm up the marinara sauce (See De Leo's Marinara sauce recipe on page TK).
3. Put a thin layer of sauce in the bottom of a large, flat baking dish.
4. Preheat the oven to 350 degrees F.
5. Place about 2 T. manicotti filling in the middle of a manicotti crepe along the middle of the crepe.
6. Roll crepe over from one side, then take opposite side and fold over so it is sealed like an envelope.
7. Place manicotti in baking dish on top of the marinara sauce.
8. Repeat process with remaining crepes and filling.
9. When baking dish is filled, add more sauce over the top.

10. Bake at 350 degrees about 20 minutes.

Notes:

1. You can substitute whole grain flour. (don't tell my mother, she might not approve.)

2. My (Maryann's) mother uses a non-stick pan to make the manicotti crepes. I don't use non-stick pans. Adjust the amount of butter depending on which type of pan is used.

3. The wax paper or plastic wrap prevents crepes from sticking together.

4. Serve with extra Parmesan cheese, if desired.

Serving size: 6 servings, approximately 15 manicotti shells

GIBBONS'S GUAJILLO CHILI

My (Nancy's) son loves to cook and create recipes. He developed this dish while he was in law school. He said this recipe is good to eat by itself (with onions and/or grated cheese), with tortilla chips, on top of corn chips, or as a sauce on top of enchiladas.

Stir well before serving.

Ingredients:

6 dried guajillo chile peppers

3.75 oz. chiles in adobo

3 lb. organic, grass-fed ground beef or venison

3 T. frozen butter, grated

12 oz. tomato sauce

1½ T. cumin

1 tsp. onion powder

2 cloves minced garlic

2 tsp. paprika

1 T. Mexican oregano

1 tsp. cayenne pepper

1 T. sea salt

3 T. masa harina

Directions:

1. Break off stems of guajillo chiles and remove seeds.

2. Place chiles in saucepan and cover with water.

3. Simmer 30 minutes. Reserve cooking liquid when finished.

4. Purée chiles in blender with chiles in adobo and enough cooking liquid to make a smooth paste.

5. Separately, in a skillet, sear meat with grated frozen butter until meat is gray on outside. (This may need to be done in batches.)

6. Transfer meat to large pot and combine with chile puree, tomato sauce, cumin, onion powder, garlic, paprika, oregano, cayenne pepper, and salt.

7. Cover with 3½ c. of remaining chile cooking liquid.

8. Bring to a boil, then reduce to a simmer. Skim fat off top as necessary.

9. Simmer 50 minutes.

10. Dissolve masa harina in ½ cup hot water to make a paste.

11. Stir into pot.

12. Cook 30 minutes.

Notes:

1. If, at any time during cooking, the chili begins to burn, stir in ½ cup of water.

2. *Masa* is the Spanish word for dough. This

is the traditional dough used in making corn tortillas. It is made with dried corn kernels that have been soaked in limewater and then ground into a dough. Masa harina is the dough flour made from the dried masa. You can usually find this with special flours. Bob's Red Mill sells this product. (See the Resources.)

Serving size: 6 servings

gluten-free

GLADYS'S IRISH STEW

My (Maryann's) dear friend Chris's mother (Gladys) was known for her delicious Irish stew.

Ingredients:

1½ lb. organic grass-fed chuck beef

2 T. vegetable oil

2½ tomato sauce

2½ c. water

3 large potatoes

2 medium onions

3 carrots, sliced

Sea salt to taste

Pepper to taste

Directions:

1. Cut chuck beef into cubes.
2. Heat oil in a pot and add the beef cubes.
3. Brown beef on all sides.
4. Drain off oil/grease.
5. Add tomato sauce and water.
6. When meat is almost cooked, add potatoes, onions, carrots, salt, and pepper, and cook until tender.

Variations:

1. Substitute potatoes with color, like purple or red skinned, for white potatoes.

2. Substitute pure, extra-virgin, organic coconut oil for vegetable oil for a healthier stew.

Serving size: 4–6 servings

GRANDMA VIOLET TERRANOVA'S FRIED CHICKEN

My (Maryann's) grandmother was motherless from the age of 12. She taught herself to cook for her father and her sisters. She was a poet, a gambler, and a kind, funny, big-hearted woman. I remember her standing in the kitchen with a brown paper bag in her hands shaking the chicken until the bag almost popped. She said she invented Shake and Bake.

Ingredients:

8 chicken parts

2–3 eggs, depending on their size

½ c. flour seasoned with salt and pepper

Hot oil

Directions:

1. Flatten chicken parts.
2. Beat eggs.
3. Dip each chicken part in egg.
4. Put seasoned flour in a brown paper bag.
5. One at a time, put each chicken piece in the bag and shake the bag to cover chicken in flour.
6. Place chicken in hot oil.
7. Cook until brown on both sides and chicken is thoroughly cooked.

8. Drain on brown paper.

Notes:

1. My (Maryann's) grandmother used chicken breasts and thighs, and Wesson oil. Any vegetable oil can be used. I don't use canola oil.

2. I (Nancy) use coconut oil and whole-grain flour.

Serving size: 6 servings

HARRY'S LATVIAN BACON TURNOVERS

Harry Koenig (Chris's dad), who was born in Latvia, was a great cook.

Turnovers can be eaten right out of the oven or after they cool a bit.

This recipe called for a package of Pillsbury crescent rolls. The healthier choice would be to make some bread from scratch, using whole-grain, non-gluten, organic ingredients.

Ingredients:
3 strips raw organic bacon
1 medium onion, diced
Salt to taste
Pepper to taste
1 egg yolk
8 crescent rolls, uncooked, or whole-grain
  bread dough of choice (cut into 8 pieces)

Directions:
1. Cut bacon into small pieces
2. Put an equal amount of onions and bacon in the middle of flattened dough.
3. Roll dough with mixture in the middle.
4. Brush lightly with egg yolk on top/middle of roll.
5. Bake according to directions on package,

or at 350 degrees F until the bread is lightly brown on top.

Note: Choose the best organic brand bacon you can find.

Serving size: 8 servings

gluten-free

HELEN'S GRILLED SALMON

Helen Roche is one of my (Maryann's) dearest friends. She lives in Mocollop, Ireland, with her handsome and brilliant husband, Marcus. Helen had a catering company in Ireland, she cooked for several bands, including U2 in their early days.

Ingredients:

2 tsp. fresh ginger, minced

2 tsp. garlic cloves, minced

2–4 T. plum sauce

4 wild salmon filets or salmon steaks

Directions:

1. Mix ginger, garlic, and plum sauce.
2. Pour marinade over salmon filets or steaks.
3. Let sit 30 minutes.
4. Remove salmon from marinade and place on grill or in baking dish.
5. Grill or broil at 350 degrees F 15 minutes. Do not overcook.

Note: Helen likes Sharwoods plum sauce, but any other plum sauce works, too.

Serving size: 4 servings

JUNIA'S BEEF STROGANOFF

My (Nancy's) mother, Junia, was a scratch cook. Her parents divorced when she was young. She and her two brothers stayed with their father. She took over the job of making the meals for the family. She didn't know how to cook, so she made the few things she did know, and then asked the neighbors for recipes.

One Christmas a neighbor gave her a cookbook. She was elated and made all kinds of meals using recipes from that cookbook for her father and brothers. My mother became a great cook. I grew up eating this specialty of hers. It's an easy dish to make when entertaining.

Serve this over hot, whole-grain rice.

Ingredients:
1 lb. round grass fed beef steak, cut into
    ¾-inch cubes
Sea salt to taste
Fresh-ground black pepper to taste
¾ c. whole-grain flour
2–3 T. pure, organic, extra-virgin coconut oil
1 c. onion, chopped
1 clove garlic, minced
1 (5.5 oz.) can mushrooms
1 can mushroom sauce
1 T. Worcestershire sauce

1 c. water

1 pint sour cream

Directions:
1. Season steak with sea salt and pepper.
2. Dip steak cubes in flour.
3. Brown steak cubes in hot coconut oil.
4. Add onions, garlic, mushrooms, mushroom sauce, and Worcestershire sauce.
5. Add water and simmer, covered, about a half hour, or until meat is tender. (You may need to add a little more water.)
6. Remove from heat and add sour cream.

Variations:
1. Substitute ½ c. fresh mushrooms for canned mushrooms.
2. Substitute mushroom soup for mushroom sauce.

Note: The recipe calls for fat, but I (Nancy) substituted coconut oil, so it would be a little healthier. My mother insists on using Crisco, no matter how many times I throw it out with her permission, it always ends up back in her pantry.

Serving size: 6 servings

gluten-free
ORIENTAL NINJA BURGER
This is a variation of one of Nancy's family recipes started by her nephew, Ryan.

Ingredients:
1 lb. organic, 100 percent grass-fed, lean
  ground beef or ground organic, turkey
1 organic egg, beaten
1 T. unpasteurized, organic soy sauce
¼ tsp. garlic powder
¼ tsp. freshly grated ginger
1 tsp. grated lemon peel
1 T. minced onion flakes
¼ tsp. black pepper

Directions:
1. Combine all ingredients.
2. Shape into four patties.
3. Place patties on rack in broiler pan or grill.
4. Cook 3 inches from heat about 5 minutes per side.

Serving size: 4 servings

SALMON CROQUETS

My (Nancy's) sister Mary Katherine (we all call her Myrtle) told me that she still makes Mom's Salmon Croquets. She said her family loves them really lemony.

We grew up eating these. They are delicious. Mary serves these warm with mashed potatoes and a spinach salad with cranberries, walnuts, and balsamic vinaigrette.

Ingredients:
    1 can wild, red salmon
    5–6 whole-grain saltines
    1 egg (organic)
    Fresh lemon juice to taste
     extra-virgin, organic coconut oil

Directions:
1. Remove the bones (spine) and skin from the salmon.
2. Mush salmon, saltines, egg, and lemon juice, and form croquets.
3. Turn burner to medium heat. Place about a half-inch of coconut oil in the skillet and heat coconut oil so a little drizzle of water sizzles when sprinkled onto oil.
4. Gently place croquets into oil.

5. Turn once to cook both sides until crispy and brown.
6. Remove patties from skillet to paper towel–lined plate to absorb excess oil.

Notes:
1. These are delicious the next day cold.
2. These would be a great lunch to take for school or work!

Serving size: 4 servings

vegetarian/gluten-free (if you use gluten free bread)

TOASTED CHEESE SANDWICH

I (Nancy) lived on these sandwiches when I was in London during college. When my children were growing up, these were one of their favorite things to eat. I used a sandwich toaster griddle, but you can use a skillet and something heavy to press the sandwich down when it is cooking. My children only liked it with cheese, until they got a little older. This is great served with a small cup of tomato soup.

Ingredients:
Butter or mayonnaise (optional)
2 slices whole-grain bread
2 thin slices organic cheddar cheese
1 tomato slice
1 thin onion slice
Extra-virgin, organic coconut oil

Directions:
1. Spread a tiny bit of butter or mayonnaise on a slice of bread, if using.
2. Place one slice of cheese on bread, and top with tomato, onion, and other cheese slice.
3. Top with other bread slice.
4. Melt a tiny bit of coconut oil in a frying pan and place sandwich in pan.
5. Cook until down side is a toasty brown.

6. Gently turn over sandwich and cook the other side until is toasty brown.
7. Slice on a diagonal.

Variation: Substitute your favorite cheese for cheddar.

Serving size: 1 sandwich

Side Dishes

vegetarian/vegan/gluten-free

AMANDA'S MEXICAN SALAD

My (Nancy's) daughter, Amanda, creates wonderful recipes. This is one of her best. It is high protein, has great flavor, and can be a complete meal.

Ingredients:
2 c. cooked black beans
2 T. extra-virgin olive oil
1 c. chopped cucumber
2 c. baby kale
1 avocado, sliced
1 clove minced garlic
¼ c. chopped cilantro
Sea salt to taste
Pepper to taste

Directions:
1. Warm up black beans.
2. Combine beans, olive oil, cucumber, kale, avocado, garlic, and cilantro and stir well.
3. Season with salt and pepper to taste.

Serving size: 2 servings

vegetarian

CARLOS'S POTATO TORTILLA

Serve warm or at room temperature.

Ingredients:

1 c. extra virgin organic olive oil or organic, extra-virgin coconut oil

1–2 onions, thinly sliced

4–5 potatoes (about 2 lb.), thinly sliced

1 tsp. unrefined sea salt

5 eggs

Directions:

1. Heat oil in a large, heavy skillet.
2. Cook onions, potatoes, and salt, stirring frequently, about 12 minutes or until the potatoes become tender.
3. Remove skillet from heat and set aside.
4. In a large bowl, whisk eggs.
5. Add potato mixture to eggs. (Leave excess oil in the skillet for later.) Stir well.
6. Let potato-egg mixture sit for about 5 minutes.
7. Clean any burned or brown pieces out of oil in skillet.
8. Heat skillet, with leftover oil, over medium heat.
9. When skillet is almost smoking, add potato-egg mixture and spread evenly in skillet.

10. Loosen edges with a metal spatula and shake pan so tortilla does not stick.
11. Cook until bottom of tortilla is golden brown.
12. Place a plate or flat dish over skillet, and invert skillet to transfer potato tortilla over to the plate.
13. Add another teaspoon of oil to the pan.
14. Slide potato tortilla back into the skillet, browned side up.
15. Cook until bottom half is golden brown (about 2 more minutes).

Variations:
1. Garnish with sprigs of parsley.

Notes:
1. Yukon Gold is a good choice for the potato in this recipe.
2. Spaniards serve mayonnaise with this.
3. Be careful with the heavy, hot skillet when removing the tortilla so you don't burn yourself. If you need to, use a really large spatula, and try to slide it out of the skillet onto a dish.
4. Serve salad on the side.

Serving size: 12 servings

vegetarian/vegan/gluten-free

DOTTY'S POTATOES AND GREEN BEANS

Ingredients:

2 red-skinned potatoes

1 lb. green beans, cut on a diagonal into
1½-inch lengths

2 T. extra-virgin organic olive oil

1½ tsp. balsamic vinegar

3 cloves garlic, minced

½ tsp. dried oregano

2 tsp. chopped fresh parsley

Sea salt to taste

Pepper to taste

Directions:

1. Boil potatoes in water until tender.
2. Combine cooked potatoes, cut into pieces, and add steamed green beans.
3. Mix together olive oil and vinegar.
4. Add garlic and oregano to olive oil mixture.
5. Combine olive oil mixture with potatoes and green beans, and toss.
6. Add parsley.
7. Season with salt and pepper to taste.

Variations: Serve cold.

Note: Any kind of white potato can be used for this recipe.

Serving size: 4 servings

vegetarian

DOTTY'S STUFFED ARTICHOKES

Ingredients:

4 large artichokes

2 c. Progresso Italian-style bread crumbs

1/3 c. tablespoons Locatelli cheese, grated

3 cloves garlic, minced

½ c. fresh parsley, washed well, dried, and chopped

1 8-oz. can plum tomatoes

Directions:

1. Cut off any brown parts from artichokes.

2. Wash artichokes and dry well.

3. Trim artichokes so that they sit flat in pot.

4. Mix breadcrumbs, cheese, garlic, parsley, and enough tomato to moisten the stuffing so that it holds together.

5. Gently separate and pull apart artichoke. (Don't break off the leaves. The artichoke will be whole when it's cooking.)

6. Stuff each artichoke leaf with approximately 1 T. stuffing.

7. Sit artichokes in the pot with a little water and a little tomato to steam.

8. Steam approximately 45 minutes.

Variation: Use any grated cheese. My (Mary-ann's) family likes Locatelli. (My parents had an ongoing debate about whether Locatelli was a region, a brand name, or a type of cheese. I don't remember if there was a winner.)

Note: The tomatoes make the stuffing moist and hold it together.

Serving size: 4 servings

vegetarian
DOTTY'S STUFFED MUSHROOMS
Ingredients:
1 lb. mushrooms
2 T. extra-virgin organic olive oil
2 c. Italian-style breadcrumbs
½ c. grated cheese
½ c. chopped parsley
Water

Directions:
1. Clean mushrooms well.
2. Remove mushroom stems and chop fine.
3. Sauté mushroom stems over medium heat in olive oil
4. Mix breadcrumbs, cheese, parsley, and sautéed stems.
5. Stuff mushroom tops with bread crumb mixture and place in a shallow baking pan.
6. Add just enough water to cover the bottom of the pan.
7. Bake approximately 30 minutes at 350 degrees F.

Note: Don't wash mushrooms, as it breaks them. Instead, use a damp paper towel or dust off mushrooms with a dry cloth.

Serving size: 4 servings

vegetarian/gluten-free (depending on the type of bread crumbs or flour used)

POTATO PANCAKES

Potato pancakes were one of my (Maryann's) father's favorite foods. Whenever my mother made them, he always remembered helping his mother peel the potatoes when he was a boy.

Use a potato for each person you are serving; adjust the other ingredients accordingly.

Ingredients:

Pure, organic, extra-virgin coconut oil for frying

4 c. potatoes, grated in long strips

1 onion (red or white), finely grated

2 eggs, beaten well

¼ c. beer (any type)

3 T. flour

1 T. sea salt

White pepper to taste

Dash of cayenne pepper (optional)

Applesauce, for topping or to serve on the side

Directions:

1. Preheat the oven to 200 degrees F.

2. Place oil in frying pan on stove.

3. Place grated potatoes, grated onion, eggs, beer, flour, salt, pepper, and, if using, cayenne pepper in a large bowl, and combine well.

4. Heat oil in the frying pan, until hot.
5. Place about ½ cup potato mixture gently in hot oil.
6. When potato pancakes are golden brown on both sides (about 5 minutes), gently remove them from frying pan and place in paper towel–lined baking dish to drain.
7. Place in the warm oven (or warming drawer) until ready to serve.

Variation:
1. Substitute sweet fruit chutney or sour cream for applesauce. Maryann uses both sour cream and applesauce.
2. Substitute Greek yogurt for sour cream.

Notes:
1. Yukon gold, sweet, or purple potatoes have more antioxidants in them.
2. Leave on the potato skin if you want more nutritional value.
3. You can put a few potato pancakes in oil at one time, if you have room in the pan and they don't touch each other. You want to. have enough room to turn them over carefully and cook each side until golden brown.

Serving size: 4 servings

Dips, Appetizers, Sauces, and Spreads

vegetarian/vegan

CLAIRE'S BALSAMIC BEAN DIP

My (Nancy's) niece Claire and her husband, Stefan, make this every week. It's a great appetizer and also perfect for entertaining, as it's quick and easy. More than once they've made it before dinner and eaten so much of it that they didn't eat dinner!

Ingredients:

1 (15-oz.) can cannellini (white kidney) beans, drained

2 T. extra-virgin organic olive oil

1 T. balsamic vinegar, plus extra for drizzling

1–2 T. freshly squeezed lemon juice

1–2 garlic cloves (to taste)

Sea salt to taste

Pepper to taste,

Assorted grain crudités, for serving

Whole-grain pita bread, cut into wedges, or pita chips, for serving

Directions:

1. Puree beans, olive oil, balsamic vinegar, lemon juice, and garlic in a food processor or blender until smooth.
2. Season with salt and pepper.
3. Transfer to bowl to serve with crudités and pita bread.

Serving size: 4–6 servings

vegetarian/vegan/gluten-free

DE LEO'S MARINARA SAUCE

Be sure to use a pot with a cover large enough for the two cans of tomatoes to fit when making this sauce.

Ingredients:

4 cloves garlic, minced

1/3 cup (approx.) extra-virgin olive oil

2 12-oz.cans whole Italian plum tomatoes

Pinch of sea salt

Pepper to taste

Oregano to taste

Directions:

1. Sauté garlic in olive oil. (Use enough oil to generously cover the bottom of the sauce-pan. Don't let garlic brown.)

2. Strain, through a colander, 2 cans of whole Italian tomatoes. Strain as much of the tomato as possible.

3. Add salt, pepper, and oregano.

4. Simmer about 30-40 minutes.

Variation: For a thicker sauce, add one small can tomato paste.

Notes:

1. I (Maryann) changed my recipe and don't strain the tomatoes. I break the tomatoes

with my fingers, throwing out the stem hard top and using the rest. My mother puts her tomatoes in the blender whole and pulses for about a minute. My dad didn't like the seeds. Any of these methods works well.

2. I (Maryann) use Italian brand tomatoes or the Whole Foods brand. The brand of tomatoes alters the taste. For years my mother used a can of tomato paste, and I followed her recipe. She gave up using tomato paste, and her sauce is thinner. She likes it that way. I gave up the tomato paste, too.

3. My (Maryann's) mother doesn't use a lot of oregano. Oregano is my favorite spice; I use lots of it in my sauce.

4. For an unknown reason, don't use the same brand of tomato paste and whole tomatoes.

vegetarian/gluten-free

NANCY'S GARLIC-HERB BUTTER

I (Nancy) love rich garlic-herb butter on my bread when I'm having soup or an Italian dish. I learned this from my mother when I was helping her in the kitchen during my childhood. My family spreads it on big, thick slices of French bread, then wraps them up and warms them to serve hot at dinner. It's easy and delicious. Use it as a spread, or spread it on each slice, heat the bread, and serve it buttered and warm.

Ingredients:

½ c. butter or ghee, room temperature

2 T. fresh parsley, chopped (or dried)

1 (or 2) cloves garlic, minced

¼ tsp. garlic salt

1 loaf whole-grain crusty bread, sliced

Directions:

1. Mash together butter, parsley, garlic, and garlic salt.

2. Spread on bread slices.

3. Warm bread or toast under broiler.

Note: When you feel you're getting a cold or sore throat take a raw fresh organic clove of garlic, mash it with a little butter and parsley (optional), and eat it plain, without cooking it, on a small piece of bread or cracker. Garlic has powerful medicinal properties. It is an anti-viral, anti- parasitic, anti-fungal food. This is a good recipe for avoiding colds.

Serving size: 4 servings

vegetarian/vegan/gluten-free

ROASTED GARLIC

This can be served with lamb or any meal and/ or spread on bread.

Ingredients:
4 heads garlic
extra virgin organic olive oil
Fresh herbs, such as thyme or parsley

Directions:
1. Place garlic in baking dish.
2. Drizzle with olive oil and sprinkle with fresh herbs.
3. Cook in the oven until garlic is soft, at 350 degrees F, for about one hour.

Notes: Roasted garlic is delicious on bread and, crackers or with meat dishes.

Serving size: 6 servings

Desserts

vegetarian/gluten-free

ANGIE'S FRUIT COBBLER

This recipe is from one of my (Maryann's) dearest friends, Angie Kenny. Angie owns Zen Cat, a gluten-free and vegan bakery in Greensboro, North Carolina. She grew up on a dairy farm and made this for her family. She's substituted gluten-free flour and unrefined sugar to keep it healthy.

Ingredients:
   1 stick butter
   2/3 c. unrefined sugar
   2/3 c. whole-grain, gluten-free flour
   1½ tsp. baking powder
   ¼ tsp. sea salt
   2/3 c. organic milk
   2–3 c. fruit, cut into bite-sized pieces as
      needed

Directions:
   1.   Preheat the oven to 350 degrees F.
   2.   In a casserole dish with deep sides (glass is great), melt butter in the oven. (Butter can brown, so watch that it doesn't.)
   3.   In a separate bowl, mix sugar, flour, baking powder, and salt.
   4.   Add milk and stir until moistened. (Some lumps are okay!)

5. Add fruit carefully to the baking dish, over butter. (You can distribute butter a bit by spooning it more toward the center.)

6. Pour flour mixture over fruit and spread evenly.

7. Bake uncovered in the oven until brown, about 30 minutes.

Variation: To make vegan, substitute an equal amount of dairy-free margarine for butter, and non-dairy milk such as rice or almond milk for milk.

Notes:

1. Oat flour and quinoa flour work really well in this recipe.

2. Good choices for fruit include berries, apples, pears, and peaches.

3. (Sometimes only the edges brown. Just make sure the center doughy part is baked.)

Serving size: 4 servings

vegetarian

AUNT ALMA'S PINEAPPLE UPSIDE-DOWN CAKE

My (Nancy's) Aunt Alma came to visit us several times. She taught my mother how to make pumpkin pie, and she also sent her this recipe. My mother made this upside-down cake for special occasions. I made a few ingredient adjustments to make it healthier. The original had almost three times the butter and sugar as this! You can probably use a little less sugar. This isn't the healthiest dessert, but it's delicious!

Serve with whipped cream.

Ingredients:
1 stick butter
1 c. raw turbinado sugar or xylitol
1 8-oz. can pineapple slices (with 5 T. juice reserved (or 8 ring slices of fresh pineapple)
1 5-oz. bottle cherries
¾ c. pecans, coarsely chopped
3 egg yolks
5 T. pineapple juice
1 c. whole-grain flour
2 tsp. baking powder

Directions:
1. Melt butter in a large iron skillet (or large, deep, round baking dish).

329

2. Spread turbinado sugar or xylitol over butter.

3. Lay pineapple slices over sugar.

4. Put a cherry (no stems) in the middle of each pineapple slice.

5. Sprinkle with chopped pecans.

6. Preheat the oven to 350 degrees F.

7. Beat egg yolks.

8. Add raw sugar and pineapple juice, and mix thoroughly.

9. Sift flour with baking powder, and then add to mixture.

10. Pour batter over pineapples in the skillet.

11. Bake about 45 minutes.

12. Let cool.

13. Place a cake plate over top of pan and flip it over, so cake is on the plate.

Variations:
1. Substitute walnuts for pecans.

2. Substitute coconut oil or ghee for butter.

3. Substitute dried cherries for fresh. Soak them in water to plump. (Aunt Alma's recipe called for maraschino cherries.)

Note: Oat flour is really good in this recipe.

Serving size: 10 servings

vegetarian/can be gluten-free (depending on what flour you use)

AUNT MILLIE'S YUMMY CRUMB CAKE

My (Maryann's) friend Chris said her Aunt Millie was known for her beauty and her crumb cake!

Batter Ingredients:

½ lb. butter

1 1/3 c. sugar (raw, unrefined)

2 eggs

1 c. milk

3 c. flour

4 tsp. baking powder

1 tsp. sea salt

Crumbs Ingredients:

½ lb. butter

2 tsp. vanilla

2¼ c. flour

2 tsp. baking powder

6 tsp. cinnamon

2 c. sugar (raw, organic)

Directions:

1. Preheat the oven to 400 degrees F.
2. Grease and flour a cookie sheet with sides (approximately 15.5x10.5).
3. Cream butter and sugar together.

4. Mix eggs and milk.

5. Sift flour, baking powder, and salt together.

6. Add flour mixture and egg mixture alternately to butter mixture, and beat well.

7. Place the batter in the prepared cookie sheet.

8. Use your fingers to make crumbs by combining all crumbs ingredients.

9. Sprinkle over top of batter.

10. Bake 25–30 minutes.

Variations:

1. Substitute half coconut oil for half of butter.

2. Substitute ghee for butter.

3. Substitute date sugar or xylitol for sugar.

Note: Any type of milk will work in this recipe.

Serving size: 12–14 servings

vegetarian

CRESCENT COOKIES

These are easy cookies to make with kids. I've (Maryann) made them with my nieces and nephews for the holidays.

Ingredients:

1 c. soft butter or ghee
1 T. vanilla extract
1 c. powdered sugar, plus more for sprinkling
½ tsp. sea salt
1 c. walnuts, chopped
2 c. King Arthur's unbleached all-purpose
   flour or whole-grain quinoa flour

Directions:

1. Preheat the oven to 325 degrees F.
2. Combine butter, vanilla, sugar, and salt until creamy.
3. Add walnuts, and combine.
4. Add flour and mix to make a soft dough.
5. Form teaspoon-sized balls of dough. With newly washed hands, shape balls into little crescents and place onto ungreased cookie sheet, leaving ½ inch or more between cookies.
6. Bake 15 minutes. (Do not let them get brown.)

7.   Sift powdered sugar over the cookies.

8.   Let cool.

Serving size: approximately 24 cookies

vegetarian

DOTTY'S SOUR CREAM COFFEE CAKE

Ingredients:

½ c. chopped walnuts

1 tsp. cinnamon

1/3 c. brown sugar

½ c. soft butter

1 c. sugar or xylitol

2 eggs

2 c. sifted flour

1 tsp. baking powder

1 tsp. baking soda

¼ tsp. salt

1 tsp. vanilla

1 cup sour cream

Directions:

1. Mix walnuts, cinnamon, and brown sugar, and set aside.

2. Cream butter and sugar in large bowl.

3. Add eggs.

4. Sift together and add flour, baking powder, baking soda, and salt.

5. Add vanilla and sour cream, and beat well

6. Put half of batter in a greased and floured angel food or Bundt pan.

7. Add half of walnuts, cinnamon, and brown sugar.

8. Add remaining batter and remaining walnuts, cinnamon, and brown sugar.

9. Bake at 350 degrees F 45 minutes.

Variation: Add ½ c. bittersweet chocolate chips. My (Maryann's) mother often puts chocolate chips in the topping. The chocolate melts and it's delicious.

Note: You can use whole-grain flour.

Serving size: 10–12 servings

vegetarian/gluten-free

GRANDMA'S RICE PUDDING

This is a combined recipe from both of my (Maryann's) grandmothers and one of my father's favorite desserts. I've changed some ingredients for a more vitamin-enriched dessert.

Ingredients:

½ c. brown rice, cooked

3 c. organic coconut milk

½ c. + a pinch of unrefined sugar or xylitol

½ c. raisins

1 tsp. vanilla extract

Pinch of sea salt

3 organic eggs

Dash of cinnamon

Directions:

1. Put cooked rice, milk, ½ c. sugar, raisins, vanilla, and sea salt into a large saucepan on the stove over medium heat.
2. Let thicken, stirring constantly.
3. In a separate bowl, beat eggs with a pinch of sugar.
4. Pour rice mixture into an ovenproof casserole dish.
5. Add eggs and swirl through rice mixture.
6. Sprinkle with cinnamon.

7.   Bake 30 minutes at 350 degrees F.

Variation: Substitute maple syrup for sugar.

Note: Don't overcook. It may look loose, but it will thicken after it cools.

Serving size: 4 servings

vegetarian/gluten-free

HOLIDAY CHOCOLATE CAKE

This is a cake my (Nancy's) mother makes for birthdays and other celebrations. She bakes it in a large cookie sheet with a 1-inch side. It's like a brownie with icing. Mom uses white refined flour and sugar for this recipe, but it's just as great using the healthier versions of flour, butter, and sugar. When I use quinoa flour, it is gluten-free.

Cake Ingredients:
   2 c. quinoa flour
   2 c. whole, unrefined sugar (or xylitol or date
      sugar)
   2 sticks butter
   4 T. cocoa
   1 c. water
   ½ c. buttermilk
   2 eggs
   1 tsp. aluminum-free baking soda
   1 tsp. vanilla

Directions:
   1.   Preheat the oven to 400 degrees F.
   2.   Sift together flour and sugar in a bowl.
   3.   Separately mix in a saucepan butter, cocoa, and water. Bring to a rapid boil, and then pour over flour and sugar.

4. Stir well.

5. Add buttermilk, eggs, baking soda, and vanilla, and mix well.

6. Pour cake into a well-greased 11x16 baking sheet or pan that is at least a half-inch deep.

7. Bake 20 minutes.

Variation: Substitute 12 T. coconut oil plus 4 T. ghee for butter. (I (Nancy) do this to have a healthier fat and still have the butter flavor.)

Icing Ingredients:
1 stick butter
4 T. cocoa
6 T. milk
1 box powdered sugar (or 1½ c. xylitol or date sugar)
1 tsp. vanilla extract
1 c. pecans, chopped

Directions:
1. While cake is baking, melt together and bring to a boil butter, cocoa, and milk.

2. Remove quickly from the heat.

3. Add powdered sugar, vanilla, and pecans. Beat together well.

4. Spread icing on cake as soon as it comes out of the oven and is still hot.

Variation: Substitute 4 T. coconut oil and 4 T. ghee for butter.

Note: Xylitol and date sugar are healthier choices, but they make the icing a little less smooth.

Serving size: 10–12 servings

Breads

vegetarian/gluten-free
MATTIE LOU'S ZUCCHINI BREAD

My (Nancy's) Granny (my father's mother) got this recipe from her friend, who owned the Highland Park Cafeteria in Dallas, Texas.

This bread is delicious. This is a slight variation with some healthier ingredients taken from the original recipe.

Ingredients:

2 c. whole-grain oat or quinoa flour

1½ tsp. baking powder

1 tsp. sea salt

1 tsp. cinnamon

1 c. pecans, coarsely chopped

3 eggs

1 c. organic extra-virgin coconut oil

1 3/4 c. raw, unrefined sugar or xylitol

3 tsp. vanilla

2 c. zucchini squash, peeled and grated coarsely, and set aside to drain

Directions:

1. Preheat the oven to 400 degrees F.
2. Mix together flour, baking powder, salt, cinnamon, and pecans.
3. Beat eggs well until light and fluffy.
4. Mix eggs with remaining ingredients, including flour mixture and grated squash.

5. Grease and flour a loaf pan.

6. Bake about 45 minutes. (Use the toothpick test for doneness.)

Note: The original recipe called for white refined wheat flour. I (Nancy) substitute gluten-free flours in recipes. Non-gluten flours taste delicious and work great. Quinoa, oat, and teff flour are my favorites. Teff is high protein. Quinoa is a complete protein. Oat is a non-gluten flour, but it needs to be labeled gluten-free, because it is frequently stored and transported in the same containers or silos as wheat, and it will become contaminated with the gluten. Oat flour will make the bread a little less sticky than the whole wheat.

Serving size: 8 servings

Part III
Additional Information

Dehydration

Staying hydrated is important, especially for older people.

Drinking plain water is the best way to remain hydrated, but other fluids work, too. Coconut water is great for hydration, as it has lots of electrolytes and is sugar free.

My (Maryann's) father was drinking Gatorade (recommended by his doctors), but Luanne Pennesi, a holistic nurse, told my dad to give up Gatorade and drink coconut water. My dad didn't like coconut water, so we give him plenty of other fluids, especially juices, all diluted with water.

Several times over the last two years of his life my dad became weak and couldn't move, all caused by dehydration. We took him to the hospital each time, and when he was given IV fluids he became alert and strong. Be careful with dehydration for your family members; it sneaks up on the elderly.

One of my brothers told me when his mother-in-law was in her 80s he and my sister-in-law thought she was having a stroke. She could barely speak and was unable to stand. They brought her to the hospital, and all her symptoms were from dehydration. When she had fluids she was up and around, sparkly and chatting with them as though nothing had happened. They were amazed at what lack of fluids could do. However, be careful in the hospital. My father was also over-hydrated, causing severe problems medical problems.

The amount of water one should drink is determined by the color and odor of the urine: If the urine has a high color and a strong odor, drink more water. Keep the urine light in color.

Bowel Movements

A s indelicate as it is to talk about, bowel movements were a frequent subject around my (Maryann's) house. As people age, it can become a problem. A nurse suggested we try giving my dad a shot-sized glass full of warmed-up prune juice (with the pulp) every day. It worked well. Dates are also a natural laxative.

Food wise, the best thing for constipation is the juice from watermelon rind. (A juicer is required. A powerful blender will work, too, but you will have to strain the mixture or drink it with all of the fiber.)

Pick a watermelon with deep color (rich in anti-oxidants). Wash the watermelon really well, cut the rind off, and juice away! Add a pinch of whole sea salt for added minerals. The watermelon and watermelon rind are full of natural electrolytes. Adding the salt will help you absorb the hydrating waters from the juice. Drink this mixture. If you can walk around, or get some sort of body movement, that helps to get the system moving.

For diabetics or anyone worried about high blood sugar, adding some juice from fresh string beans will make the drink less sugary, reducing the blood sugar impact . "One cup of string bean skin is equal to at least one unit of insulin."[32] I (Nancy) made this mixture for Larry Hagman when he was in the hospital and none of the medications for constipation that they were giving him were working. I made this for him and it worked quickly and efficiently.

Recipe

1½ c. watermelon rind juice

½ c. juice from the watermelon

Pinch of whole sea salt

½ c. whole string bean juice (from fresh string beans; addition for diabetics)

Flowers and Plants

Flowers and plants lift the spirit and clean the air.

Surround yourself and your loved ones with fresh flowers and/or plants. Plants add vibrancy and fresh air, and change the feeling of a room.

I (Nancy) read a study many years ago that said adding a vase of fresh flowers to a room made people's attitudes happier and more positive. I add flowers and plants to my space and to the spaces of those I love.

When a loved one is in a nursing home, hospital, or small place where they can't get out much, it's an easy thing to add a plant or vase of flowers to the room.

Plants increase humidity, reducing some of the drying effects of indoor heaters and air systems.

Take a small cutting from the garden of mint or ivy and put it in water, and—presto!—you have a plant that will create a new feeling to the room.

When my (Nancy's) former husband (an environmental trial lawyer) was conducting environmental impact studies on air quality, I learned that plants are masters at cleaning certain toxins from the air.

Ficus plants are great at cleaning formaldehyde out of the air. Low-light plants like the ivy plants are great to use in general. Many low-light plants that have shallower root systems are the easiest and most beneficial for removing toxins from indoor air.

Hair

Eat for your hair! Hair loss may be from a deficiency of Vitamin B and other nutrients. A lack of essential fatty acids can also affect the hair. A lack of Vitamin B6, folic acid, magnesium, sulfur, zinc, and multiple nutrients in the Vitamin B complex can result in hair thinning or hair loss.

Foods rich in B vitamins are brewer's yeast, wheat germ, and lecithin. Beans and seafood are also high in protein and B vitamins. Zinc works in cell reproduction and hormone balance, affecting hair growth.

If the body is low on zinc, hair follicles can become weak. Foods heavy in zinc are seafood and nuts. Some products have zinc in them. Recently some denture creams have been found to have large amounts of zinc. Too much zinc is not good, either. Before taking a zinc supplement, have your zinc level checked, especially if you are using a denture cream and have a concern. Some companies have started making denture cream without added zinc.

Silica, found in the skin of potatoes, green and red peppers, cucumbers, bean sprouts, and raw oats, also has health benefits.

Vitamin E is another important element of healthy hair, improving scalp circulation because of its increased blood-oxygenation properties. Avocados, kiwi fruit, nuts, seeds, and olive oil are good sources of Vitamin E.

Vitamin A protects hair follicles, and can be found in carrots, spinach, and unrefined, cold-pressed seed oils, such as flax, walnut, and pumpkin.

Iodine is also essential to healthy hair. Beneficial iodine is found in sea vegetables (seaweed), cabbage, pine nuts, and millet. Sea vegetables are a good source of iodine, calcium, phosphorus, iron, potassium, and minerals; varieties of sea vegetables are dulse, nori, wakame, and kelp.

Omega 3's, one of the essential fatty acids are another way to promote healthy skin and hair. They are crucial in transporting and breaking down cholesterol, boosting the immune system, and supporting the thyroid and adrenal glands.

Chia seeds and hemp seed oil contain large amounts of Omega 3 oils. Cold-pressed flax seed oil could be one of the best remedies. It contains the right proportion of alpha-linolenic acid (Omega 3) and non-rancid linolenic acid, which is good because they work best as a combination.

Some other essential fatty acid sources are walnuts, avocados, almonds, pecans, pumpkin seeds, hazelnuts, pine nuts, sesame seeds, olives, and their respective oils.

Dandruff is an excess of protein and saturated fat the body is trying to expel. Also, dry, rough skin, like dandruff, is an indication of gluten intolerance. If you have been battling dandruff, get testing for gluten intolerance or changing your diet to gluten free, and see if that helps.

Too much simple sugar, hormone imbalance, excess cholesterol, and excess toxins in the body can all cause the hair to gray. The root of the hair cannot produce melanin. The cells in the root are deprived of nutrients and starved to death. If the body is trying to heal or prevent depletions in other parts of the body, the body will send the nutrients to the most vital place. Hair is not a vital organ, so it's one of the areas from which nutrients are taken. This is why hair and nails are indicators of health. When health is vibrant, hair and nails will be strong and thick.

Laughter Is the Best Medicine

I (Maryann) spent time with my father watching old TV shows. He relaxed when watching the comedies, and I felt better, too. We didn't concentrate on his illness in those moments when we were laughing. He had a great, hearty laugh, and I always felt it helped his breathing. He was able to breathe more deeply when he was laughing. This is an entirely non-scientific observation.

We watched DVDs of *Green Acres* and *Fawlty Towers,* two of his favorite shows. We also watched lots of comedy clips on YouTube. Sometimes he laughed so hard it looked like he was crying!

Here's a list of some comedy shows and clips you can find on YouTube:

Fawlty Towers
Laurel and Hardy
Charlie Chaplin
The Carol Burnett Show
Abbott and Costello
Dean Martin Roasts
Monty Python
Green Acres
And there are many more!

Nancy's family likes *Mister Ed,* Burns and Allen, Jack Benny, and *I Dream of Jeannie.*

Lighting

L ighting affects our health. Eye strain is wors- ened by bad lighting. Full-spectrum lighting will ease eye strain, because it more closely resembles true sunlight and has a softer glow than fluorescent lighting. Full-spectrum lighting makes reading easier and creates a healthier environment, especially in the winter months when we don't get enough sunlight.

Many elderly people in small bedrooms or apartments don't have sufficient lighting or exposure to sunlight.

I (Nancy) replaced my mother's fluorescent light bulbs in her kitchen. She was skeptical, and she said, "Why do we need to change my light bulbs?" One of her light bulbs had burned out and a few of her light bulbs were mismatched, and I wanted to make them uniform. I wanted them to all be consistent. I told her about the studies I had read about how full-spectrum lighting had improved health and reading ability when put into use. Mom finally agreed to let me replaced her light bulbs. I put them in and, after a few days, she said, "Nancy, I love my new light bulbs! I didn't think it would make much difference, but I love them!" The lighting was softer and it was easier to read in that light. I replaced all of my standard light bulbs years ago with the full-spectrum lights. I immediately noticed a difference in my workspace and how much easier it was to read.

I (Nancy) have read that it's important to have sunlight actually in the eyes, without sunglasses, in order to gain the real benefits.

Some resources -

Light, Radiation and You: How to Stay Healthy by John Ott

Daylight Robbery-The Importance of Sunlight to Health by Dr. Damien Downing

Lighting-Presentation at the Learning and Brain Conference, Washington, D.C. May, 03,2000 by Kenneth Kosik and Lisa Heschons.

Effects of School Lighting on Physical and Development and School Performance. By Warren Hathaway- Journal Educational Research, v88, n4, p. 228-42, March- April 1995.

Full-spectrum light bulbs are available at Home Depot, hardware stores, Whole Foods Market, and many other stores that sell light bulbs.

Microwave Ovens

Throw out your microwave oven! Microwaving food distorts the molecular structure and destroys much of the nutrients.

My (Maryann's) father once saw a fly go into the microwave and die. After that he said he was careful about using it, and only used it to reheat coffee.

My (Nancy's) former husband, the environmental trial lawyer, read studies on microwave ovens, when they were first being introduced to the market. He never allowed a microwave in our home.

Natural and Organic Labels

What is natural, and what is organic? "Organic" means that the product was grown without the use of chemical fertilizers and pesticides. Organic standards vary from state to state in the United States, and also from country to country. A certified organic product has been certified as to organic farming standards. This means standards in the industry were met and were certified by the U.S. Department of Agriculture (USDA) and other government agencies in other countries. Nothing is absolutely pure, but it's the best standard.

Be wary of products that are labeled "natural." A chemically derived ingredient can still be labeled natural. Don't be fooled by advertising.

Non-Toxic Household Cleaners

Window Cleaner

Combine ½ cup sudsy ammonia, 1 pint rubbing alcohol, 1 teaspoon dish detergent, and 1 gallon water.

Put the mixture in a spray bottle, spray on windows, and wipe.

Instead of paper towels, use newspaper.

Note: Never mix ammonia and bleach. That is extremely dangerous, because toxic vapors can be produced.

Soft Scrub for Counters, Sinks, and Stoves

Combine 2 cups baking soda, ½ cup Castile soap, 4 teaspoons vegetable glycerin, and a few drops essential oil (lavender, peppermint, or tea tree). Store in a sealed jar.

Drain Opener

Pour ½ cup baking soda into the drain, then pour in ½ cup white vinegar. Let stand 30 minutes. Flush with boiling water.

Furniture Polish

Combine ¼ cup olive oil with ½ cup white vinegar. Add 2 teaspoons lemon juice. Apply to fur-

* indicates the recipe can be made gluten-free.

niture, and then wipe off.

Toilet Bowl Cleaner

Sprinkle the bowl of the toilet with baking soda; add in a little white vinegar. Wait 30 minutes, then scrub. You can also add in a ¼ cup borax.

Personal Care

Skin Brush

Use a skin brush when showering or bathing. Our skin pores can become clogged, so a good, thorough skin brushing (whether dry or in the shower) will help clean the pores and add circulation to the skin. Massaging, kneading, brushing, and unclogging the skin and muscle areas can break up and help release toxins. Drink lots of water to help flush out any toxins that may be released. A natural skin brush can be purchased at many stores. If you can't handle the hard one, try a soft one; eventually you can move to a harder brush that can circulate the energy and break up stagnant areas. Always work from the outside of the body toward the heart. Start at the feet and hands, and work your way toward the chest and heart area. A salt or sugar scrub can make this more cleansing and refreshing.

When you use a loofah, always use a dry loofah. Bacteria live in a moist or wet loofah. Buy two loofahs so that you will always have one that is dry to use.

I (Nancy) have even washed and dried mine in the washing machine.

Warm Towel Scrub

When I (Nancy) was a child my grandmother taught me to take a washcloth, run it under warm to hot water, place it over my face, relax, and breathe in, and then gently scrub my face with the washcloth.

A yoga teacher told me (Maryann) to scrub your body all over with a warm, wet, cotton washcloth.

Cold Water Rinse

When I (Nancy) am bathing or showering, I always turn the water colder for my final rinse. Even if just for a moment, it can seal up the pores so they don't allow dirt back in right after you have cleansed your skin. It seals in moisture and is protective to the body.

Body Lotion

Skin is absorbent. Don't put anything on your skin that you wouldn't eat.

Dental and Oral Care

When my (Nancy's) children were young I saw that mouthwashes and toothpastes contained ingredients that were not healthful. I searched for better products. It is much easier these days; I get toothpastes without fluoride. I also have toothpaste for each person. When we get the toothpaste out of the tube, we put the toothbrush up on the toothpaste opening and can spread germs to other people using that toothpaste. I also change toothbrushes every three to four weeks, and especially after someone has been ill. I buy soft-bristle brushes that don't hurt the gums.

Some mouthwashes have alcohol in them. Our mouth is the most absorbent place in our body. I use a tongue scraper. It cleans off toxins that we emit overnight.

I (Maryann) use Mitoku's dentie black tooth powder, made from eggplant and sea salt. The dentie tooth powder works well at getting out bacteria and plaque in your mouth. I never gave this to my parents—brushing with black tooth powder is a little too much for them!

I (Maryann) read this on the internet; it was written by a holistic dentist:

> "Do NOT use regular toothpaste. Most of it has fluoride—which clearly is a poison and not intended for human use. Instead use a mixture of six parts of baking soda to one part of Real Salt or Sea Salt. Place them in a blender and mix for 30 seconds then place in a container to use.

> "Wet the tip of your index finger and

place a SMALL amount of the salt and soda mixture on the gums. Starting with the upper outside gums and then the inside of the upper, followed by the lower outside of the gums then the lower inside. Spit out the excess. After 15 minutes rinse your mouth. This mixture is incredibly effective at killing the bacteria and parasites that cause plaque."

Look on the box of the toothpaste you are buying. If it says to call the poison control if swallowed and/or "Keep out of the reach of children," I (Nancy) would start buying a new brand of toothpaste. Many of the most popular brands say this on their packaging box, but not on the tube itself.

Bathing/Bath Water Soaks

Add whole, sea salt to the bath. The minerals in the sea salt relax the muscles and ease stiff joints. Soaking in a bath of sea salt combined with baking soda and bentonite clay can help remove radiation from the body. When adding ingredients like epsom salt or sea salt, add them while filling the tub. Add a couple of tablespoons or more of organic apple cider vinegar (which helps regulate the pH of the body) to the bathtub mixture as well. When you get into the tub, add essential oils to the bathtub, so the oil fragrance doesn't dissipate before getting in. The fragrance is part of the aromatherapy. Use oils like eucalyptus, lavender, rosemary, or lemon balm. If I (Nancy) am having a footbath, I like to add peppermint oil to the water to refresh and stimulate.

Rose or other flower petals or herbs like lavender, rosemary, or lemon balm wrapped in cheesecloth or a small muslin bag (and tied so the petals don't fall out) are wonderfully fragrant and a healthy addition to a bath.

Therapeutic Bath Soak

This is a soak that will rejuvenate. The skin is the body's largest organ, and the chlorophyll-rich nutrients will soak into the body through the skin. Add the essential oil just before you step into the bath so the aroma is fresh.

Ingredients:

2 c. or more fresh green chlorophyll-rich juice

A few drops of your favorite essential oil, like eucalyptus

Directions: Soak about 10 to 15 minutes.

Variation: Add ¼ cup mineral salt to this bath for additional nutrient benefit.

Note: A body lotion of almond oil or coconut oil after the bath feels wonderful.

Face Masks and Facial Washes

Honey is antibacterial and can be used for a hydrating face mask and face wash. Buy organic, raw honey and put it all over the face and let it stay on 10–20 minutes and then wash it off with a warm wash cloth.

Yogurt is a calming facemask. You can combine yogurt and honey for a hydrating and soothing facemask.

Vitamin-Rich Facial Mask

A facial mask rich in vitamins helps replenish skin collagen, helps diminish age spots, and improves the texture of skin.

Ingredients:

1 or ½ ripe avocado

1 small carrot, pureed or steamed

1 egg yolk

2 T. honey

2 T. plain yogurt

1 tsp. aloe vera juice

Directions:

1. Mash all ingredients in a bowl.
2. Smooth all over face. (Always be careful around the eye area; don't get too close to the eyes.)
3. Let dry 15–20 minutes.
4. Rinse off with warm water, then splash

with cool water to close pores.

5. Moisturize with organic raw coconut oil.

Bedtime or Stress-Reducing Aids

Put some fresh lavender in a small muslin bag and tie it with a string or ribbon. Put this in a pillowcase for an aromatic, stress-reducing, and calming sleep.

You can also put lavender or rosemary in the pockets of your clothes to stay fresh smelling through the season. I (Nancy) used to give lavender or rosemary sprigs to my children and my first husband to put in their pockets when they were leaving for the day. I told them to take it out and smell it throughout the day, and it would give them a mental lift—an aromatherapy lift. Lavender also repels moths.

Body or Face Sprays

These sprays lift the spirit! To infuse water, simply put some fresh herbs in a bottle of water and let it sit for a few hours. (Putting this in the sun is good but not necessary; it can absorb the solar rays from the sun). After it has infused, use a strainer to remove the herbs.

Rosemary and peppermint stimulate the brain and can be used when you wish to stay alert or mentally focused. Lavender is calming and soothing. For someone who is bed-ridden or not well, this can be refreshing.

Put the spray bottle in the refrigerator. When you want to feel refreshed, spray your face or your body.

Hair

I (Maryann) stopped using store-bought shampoo (to my mother's horror), as most shampoos have chemicals in them. I use homemade shampoo.

Shampoo

Ingredients:

2 T. extra-virgin olive oil

1 egg

1 T. lemon or lime juice

1 tsp. unrefined, organic apple cider vinegar

Directions:

1. Combine ingredients in a blender.
2. Blend well.

Notes:

1. 1. Use just as you would regular shampoo.

Conditioner

Ingredients:

1 egg yolk

½ tsp. extra- virgin olive oil

3/4 c. lukewarm water

Directions:

1. Beat egg yolk until thick and white.
2. Add oil and mix well.
3. Add water and mix well.
4. Massage into clean, damp hair.
5. Rinse with plenty of warm water after about 10 minutes.

My (Nancy) daughter and I make hair conditioner treatments out of various cold-pressed oils. Sometimes we leave it in overnight and sometimes, when we want it to be especially deep, we will put a heating cap on for about 20 minutes. This lets it really soak into the hair and scalp.

Warts and Brown Skin Spots

A folk remedy for warts or brown spots is to use the inside of a banana peel. Rub the inside of the peel on a wart or brown spot every night. Results are usually seen in about two weeks.

Sleep

S leep has become a problem for many people. As we get older, we don't produce as much melatonin, a hormone that helps us sleep. Melatonin is produced by our pineal gland. This hormone helps maintain our body's circadian rhythm—our internal clock—which tells our body when to sleep and when to awaken. If we don't have enough melatonin, our body will pull it from our serotonin reserve in order to produce it. Melatonin helps regulate other hormones as well. Dr. Gary Massad told me that the melatonin works better if you take about a half-milligram of it around 3 or 4 in the afternoon.

Melatonin works much better if you have enough Vitamin B in your system. If you are concerned about Vitamin B, check with your doctor. If you are a vegan or vegetarian, you may want to make sure your B vitamin levels are optimum.

Digestion can also create a problem with sleep. If you are having a digestion problem, try lying down on your left side. Ancient Ayurveda has been suggesting this position for centuries to aid in digestion. It also helps with the spine or back pain to put a pillow between the knees and also under the head, when sleeping or lying down.

Make your bedroom a quiet place to sleep. Keep all electromagnetic devices (computer, TV, cell phone, etc.) out of you bedroom, so you won't be absorbing electromagnetic waves while you are sleeping.

Also, make your bedroom very dark. Even the smallest light can disrupt sleep.

About 30 minutes or more before you go to sleep, meditate on things that are uplifting. Write down a "to do" list for the things you want to do the next day. This will get them off of your mind. Write a page or two of things you are grateful for in a journal. Read an uplifting book. Avoid news programs or violent shows before sleep. Tell yourself that you go to sleep easily. Remind the mind that it is time to rest. Do some deep breathing with your meditation. If you breathe really deeply down into the diaphragm, it will help you to de-stress and relax.

Books Recommended by the Authors

Maryann's Recommendations

Love Your Body by Viktoras Kulvinskas

Macrobiotics: An Invitation to Health and Happiness by George Ohsawa

The Vegetarian Epicure by Anna Thomas

Vital Foods by H.E. Kirschner

The Maker's Diet by Jordan S. Rubin

Patient Heal Thyself by Jordan S. Rubin

The Self-Healing Cookbook by Kristina Turner

Nature Has a Remedy by Bernard Jensen
(I bought this book for five cents at the library, and it has been a great resource. I highly recommend it.)

Cooking with Herbs and Spices by Craig Claiborne

The Gaylord Hauser Cookbook by Gaylord Hauser

Natural Diet for Folks Who Eat: Cooking with Mother Nature by Dick Gregory

The Body Ecology by Donna Gates

Living in the Moment by Gary Null

Diet for a Small Planet by Frances Moore Lappe

The Healing Power of Natural Foods by May Bethel

Herbs for the Kitchen by Irma Goodrich Mazza

Moosewood Cookbook by Mollie Katzen

Essentials of Classic Italian Cooking by Marcella Hazan

Simply Reflexology by Claire Wynn

Lidia's Italian-American Kitchen by Lydia Matticchio Bastianich

The Joy of Juicing by Gary Null and Shelly Null

The Great Life Diet by Denny Waxman

The Prophet by Khalil Gibran (This was one of my father's favorite books.)

Nancy's Recommendations

How to Be a Healthy Vegetarian by Nancy Addison

Genetic Roulette by Jeffrey Smith

Healing with Whole Foods by Paul Pritchard

Light, Radiation and You: How to Stay Healthy by John Ott

Daylight Robbery: The Importance of Sunlight to Health by Dr. Damien Downing

Staying Healthy with Nutrition: The Complete Guide to Diet and Nutritional Medicine by Elson M. Haas, MD

Blink by Malcolm Gladwell

Prescription for Nutritional Healing: A Practical A–Z reference to Drug-Free Remedies Using vitamins, Minerals, Herbs & Food Supplements (3rd Edition) by Phyllis A. Balch, CNC

Coconut Cures by Bruce Fife, ND

The Raw Food Detox Diet by Natalia Rose

Food and Healing by Annemarie Colbin

Food for Life by Neal Barnard, MD

Foods that Fight Pain by Neal Barnard, MD

The Sunfood Diet Success System by David Wolfe

The Hippocrates Diet and Health Program by Dr. Ann Wigmore

The Natural Hygiene Handbook by the American Natural Hygiene Society

There Is a Cure for Diabetes by Gabriel Cousens, MD

Eat, Drink and Be Healthy by Walter C. Willett, MD

The Anti-Inflammation Zone by Dr. Barry Sears

Listen from the Inside Out: An Everyday Guide to the Secrets of Sound Healing by Sharon Carne

Program for Reversing Heart Disease: The Only System Scientifically Proven to Reverse Heart Disease Without Drugs or Surgery by Dr. Dean Ornish

Raw Food for Everyone: Essential Techniques and 300 Simple-to- Sophisticated Recipes by Alissa Cohen with Leah J. Dubois

The Secret Life of Water by Masaru Emoto

Living on Live Food by Alissa Cohen

The Mcdougall Program for a Healthy Heart: A Live-Saving Approach to Preventing and Treating Heart Disease by John A. McDougall, MD; recipes by Mary McDougall

Water: For Health, for Healing, for Life: You're Not Sick, You're Thirsty! by Dr. Fereydoon Batmanghelidj

Water Cures: Drugs Kill: How Water Cured Incurable Diseases by Dr. Fereydoon Batmanghelidj

You Can Heal Your Life by Louise L. Hay

You'll See it When You Believe It by Dr. Wayne Dyer

Your Body's Many Cries for Water by Dr. Fereydoon Batmanghelidj

The Food Revolution by John Robbins

Appendix A
Recipe Index

Appendix B
Vegetarian Recipe Index

* indicates the recipe can be made vegetarian.

Appendix C
Vegan Recipe Index

* indicates the recipe can be made vegan.

Appendix D
Gluten-Free Recipe Index

* indicates the recipe can be made gluten-free.

* indicates the recipe can be made gluten-free.

* indicates the recipe can be made gluten-free.

* indicates the recipe can be made gluten-free.

* indicates the recipe can be made gluten-free.

* indicates the recipe can be made gluten-free.

Appendix E
Raw Recipe Index

* indicates the recipe can be made raw.

Resources

Commodities Natural Market
165 1st Ave
New York, NY 10003
(212) 260–2600
www.CommoditiesNaturalMarket.com/

Whole Foods Market

This store carries many high-quality products and foods, including meats. It's a great source for supplements, home supplies, body and bath supplies, as well as food. They told me that they are very careful to avoid genetically modified foods for use in their own brand of product, even if it is not certified organic.

www.WholeFoodsMarket.com/

Natural Grocers

This store sells organic produce and products, often at great prices. They have locations in Idaho, Kansas, Missouri, Nebraska, New Mexico, Oklahoma, Texas, Utah, and Wyoming.

www.NaturalGrocers.com/

Central Market

This is a Texas store at the moment, but they are expanding. They have mail order, cooking classes, and a variety of other services.

www.CentralMarket.com/Home.aspx

New Frontiers

This store is a supporter of non–genetically modified foods. I have found some really nice organic produce and products at this market. They have locations in Arizona and California.

NewFrontiersMarket.com/

Sprouts

This store sells organic produce and products. It is based in Arizona and has stores in California, Texas, Colorado, and Arizona.

Sprouts.com/

Trader Joe's

They carry some organic produce and products at this market. Their private label is from non–genetically modified sources.

www.TraderJoes.com/

Vitamins

Buy vitamins made with whole organic food. The body reads that much better than isolated chemicals.

I (Nancy) buy Garden of Life and New Chapter Organics. They have a variety of choices for all kinds of vitamins, minerals, etc.

We (Maryann's family) gave my father Floradil MultiVitamins, recommended by Luanne Pennesi, a holistic nurse.

New Chapter Organics

A variety of whole-food-based and organic products.

www.NewChapter.com

Garden of Life

A variety of whole-food-based and organic products.

Nancy is a distributor for Garden of Life. If you would like to order from Nancy, her website is www.OrganicHealthyLifestyle.com.

She can order you products that are hard to find at the grocery store.

www.GardenOfLife.com

Magnesium

Ancient Minerals
Ultra-pure magnesium oil.
www.MagneticClay.com

Peter Gillham's Natural Vitality - Natural Calm

www.PeterGillham.com

Home Delivery and Mail-Order Foods

Greenling

This is a local Texas Company that has home delivery, but also has mail order for all kinds of foods, appliances, kits, etc. Check it out!

Austin: (512) 440–8449

San Antonio: (210) 805–1919

Dallas/Fort Worth: (469) 656–7913

Houston: (713) 364–0099

www.Greenling.com/home

Natalia Rose and her Detox the World site

Natalia sells food for delivery just about any-where. She's located in New York City. She has other resources for juicing, getting detoxed, colonics, etc. She also has books and recipes.

www.DetoxTheWorld.com/

Veggie Brothers

100% vegan/vegetarian online store. They use the best and freshest natural and organic ingredients available. None of their ingredients have been genetically modified. 100% organic. 100% wheat- and gluten-free.

(877) 834–2655

www.VeggieBrothers.com

Local Harvest

www.LocalHarvest.org/

Organic Authority

This website can help you locate locally grown, organic foods.

www.OrganicAuthority.com/

Raw Foods

Live Live
They sell lots of raw organic food, make-up, etc.
They do mail order as well.
261 East 10th St.
New York, NY
(212) 505–5604
E-mail: info@live-live.com

Brad's Raw Foods
He sells raw organic foods.
E-mail : brad@bradsrawfoods.com

Garden of Life
www.GardenOfLife.com

Snack Bars

Raw Crunch Bars
They come in cranberry, chocolate, goji berry, and blueberry.
RawCrunchBar.myshopify.com/

Fruits of Life by Garden of Life
These organic raw bars are delicious.
www.GardenOfLife.com

Sprouting: Seeds, Information, and Equipment

The Hippocrates Health Institute

This is a great resource for seeds, equipment, raw food, vegan food, etc.

1443 Palmdale Court

West Palm Beach, FL 33411

www.HippocratesHealthInstitute.com

Got Sprouts

www.GotSprouts.com

Sprout People

www.SproutPeople.com

Grow NYC

(212) 788–7900

www.GrowNYC.org/greenmarket

Blenders and Juicers

NOTE: Juicers for wheat grass are different from regular juicers.

Healthy Juicer

The Healthy Juicer has a hand-crank juicer. This site sells professional kitchen equipment and it's competitively priced.

HealthyJuicer.com/

Instawares

www.Instawares.com

Vitamix

Vitamix has a seven-year warranty. I (Nancy) have used one for over 12 years and it is still going strong.

www.Vitamix.com

Breville

Breville has some good choices that are durable. www.BrevilleUSA.com/

Blend Tec

My (Maryann's) friend recommends the Blend Tec blender. She says it can blend anything, and it's not too expensive.

www.BlendTec.com/

Foods

Grains, Breads, Crackers and Pastas

Gluten-Free Pasta

Tinkyana Rice Pasta

This brand is very good and not mushy when cooked.

www.nextag.com/tinkyada-rice-pasta/compare-html?nxtg=7c750a24051b-CF63729B7EA53C31

Whole-Grain Pasta

Bionaturae - certified organic

www.Bionaturae.com

DeBoles Organic and All-Natural Pastas

My daughter and I love their spelt pasta.
www.DeBoles.com/

Annie's Organic

My kids love their shells with real aged cheddar. Though some of their products are made with whole-grain ingredients, others are not.
www.Annies.com

Doctor Kracker

These are organic, whole-grain crackers in a variety of flavors.
www.DrKracker.com

Mary's Gone Crackers

These crackers are organic, kosher, non-GMO, whole-grain, vegan, and wheat-free; contain no hydrogenated oils; and are manufactured in a gluten-free, dairy-free, nut-free facility.
www.MarysGoneCrackers.com

Wholly Wholesome

They make organic whole-wheat or spelt pie crust shells.
www.WhollyWholesome.com

Udi's

Delicious gluten-free breads.

I (Nancy) like the chia seed bread, and I toast it.

UdisGlutenFree.com/

Alvarado Street Bakery

This company makes delicious organic, whole-grain breads. Outside of California, their breads can be found in the freezer section of the market. Alvarado Street Bakery is located just north of San Francisco in Sonoma County. Their products are sold in the United States, Canada, and Japan.

www.AlvaradoStreetBakery.com

Tru Roots

This company has a variety of products including sprouted whole grains in bulk.

www.TruRoots.com/

Shiloh Farms

Shiloh Farms is a good source for organic whole grains.

www.ShilohFarms.com/

Bob's Red Mill

Bob's Red Mill is carried at most grocery stores. Bob's Red Mill sells a variety of grains and flours. (Bob's Red Mill carries masa harina, used in Gibbons's Guajillo Chili recipe.)

www.BobsRedMill.com/

Oats

Gluten Free Oats, LLC
578 Lane 9
Powell, WY 82435
(307) 754–7041

Cereal

Ezekiel 4.9 doesn't have a lot of added sugar. Sprouted Whole Grain Cereal - Almond_

Food for Life Baking Company
(800) 797–5090
www.FoodForLife.com

Alternative Milk

Almond Milk

Pacific Foods
Nancy likes the unsweetened vanilla.
www.PacificFoods.com

Apple Cider Vinegar

Braggs
Braggs makes raw organic vinegar and soy sauce as well as many other products.
www.Bragg.com

Organicville Foods

Organic stone-ground mustard.
OrganicvilleFoods.com

Hain Safflower Mayonnaise

This is the mayonnaise that Nancy uses.
www.HainPureFoods.com/index.php

Aloe Vera Juice Drink

AloeXtra

Sold by healthcare practictioners.
Life Nutrients
Dallas, TX
(888) 999–6690
www.AloeXtra.net

Green Concentrated Food Powder

Sun Warrior

www.SunWarrior.com/ormus-greens/

Garden of Life

www.GardenofLife.com

Sea Salt

Nancy's Sensational Sea Salt Seasoning

Sensational Sea Salt Seasoning is patent pending and created by Nancy Addison. This proprietary seasoning blend of mineral and nutrient-dense, whole, raw, organic food is made up of the finest whole, mineral-rich sea salts, sea kelps, and Omega 3 and Vitamin E rich seeds. The combination helps boost the absorption of the iodine from the ingredients. Iodine is the main nutrient that supports the thyroid gland. Use in place of your normal salt.

www.OrganicHealthyLifestyle.com
www.SensationalSeaSalt.com

Sugar Alternatives

Stevia

Sunrider

Nancy likes the Sunrider brand of stevia (Nancy).

You can order it from Nancy by e-mailing Nancy at nancy@OrganicHealthyLifestyle.com.

Sweet Leaf

Makers of Sweetleaf Sweetener®
1203 W. San Pedro St.
Gilbert, AZ 85233
(480) 921–1373
(800) 899–9908
www.SweetLeaf.com/

Xylitol

Find xylitol in grocery stores in the sugar section.
www.NowFoods.com

Cleanse

Yerba Prima
Kalenite cleansing herbs and psyllium husks.
www.YerbaPrima.com

Coffee Alternatives

Teeccino Caffé, Inc.
P.O. Box 40829
Santa Barbara, CA 93140
(800) 498–3434
(805) 966–0999 (outside the United States and Canada)
Teeccino.com/category/11/Herbal-Coffees.html

Teas

Tulsi Tea
Organic India
www.OrganicIndia.com

Yogi Tea
Good selection of organic teas.
www.YogiProducts.com

Mountain Rose Herbs
They have an amazing selection of rarer teas, herbs, oils, information, etc.
www.MountainRoseHerbs.com/

Celestial Seasonings Tea
www.CelestialSeasonings.com

Kombucha Tea

GT's Organic Raw Kombucha
(877) RE-Juice
www.GTsKombucha.com

Organic Probiotic Drinks

Kevita
Raw coconut probiotic drink.
http://Kevita.com/

Inner-eco
A coconut, power-packed probiotic kefir.
www.Inner-Eco.com

High Country
www.HighCountryKombucha.com

Meal Substitutes and Protein Powders

Garden of Life
Garden of Life has both meal substitutes and protein powders that are raw, certified organic, gluten-free, and vegan.
www.GardenOfLife.com

Organic Information

Organic Authority

This is a blog, but it has some really good information about food, etc. on it.

www.OrganicAuthority.com/

Meat, Egg, and Dairy

Ghee

I (Nancy) use this frequently instead of butter. Ghee is sold at grocery stores in the international food area or baking area. It is sold non-refrigerated, but you refrigerate it after it is opened.

Organic Ghee by Purity Farms

www.PurityFarms.com

Patches of Star Dairy

Nazareth, PA

Sold at the Union Square Farmers' Market in New York City. Alex Hushour helped us when we shopped there. They sell raw goat cheese of all kinds, pasteurized goat cheese, and fabulous goat feta.

http://www.Facebook.com/pages/Patches-of-Star-Dairy/136778723035401

Rehoboth Ranch

Rehoboth Ranch is located approximately 45 miles northeast of Dallas, Texas. The Robert and

Nancy Hutchins family raise beef, lamb, chicken, turkey, pork, eggs, and raw goat milk using organic and free-range production methods. They are not certified organic, but they do everything organically.

2238 County Road 1081
Greenville, TX 75401
(903) 450–8145
www.RehobothRanch.com/

Texas Daily Harvest

E-mail: txdayharvest@yahoo.com
(903) 335–1758

JuHa Ranch

Natural (without hormones or antibiotics) meats and eggs. They use sustainable practices.
(903) 695–2684
www.JuHaCattleCompany.com

Dis & Dat Organic Farm

Pasture-raised organic eggs.
(254) 578–9042

Busy B's Market

Organic pork and chicken, raw milk, butter, yogurt, homemade ice cream, cheese, and organic eggs.
(817) 965–0258

Arcadian Pastures
E-mail: ArcadianPastures@hotmail.com
(518) 339–6076

Beacon Natural Market
(845) 838–1288
BeaconNaturalMarket.com

Hemlock Hill Farm
(914) 733–2810

Woody's All Natural
Hormone-free, grass-fed, free-range. Not certified organic.
(845) 534–1111
WoodysAllNatural.com

Butter Bliss
(646) 300–4714
www.ButterBliss.com

Spiritual Oils and Sprays

Dean Vanderslice
Essential oils for home cleaning, etc.
www.EditsInteriors.com

Spiritual Creations™
Larry makes essential oil blends of all types. He makes me a special blend to wear as a perfume.
c/o Miracles of Joy

701 S. Old Orchard Lane
Suite C
Lewisville, TX 75067
(972) 221–8080
E-mail: Larry@SpiritualCreationsOils.com
www.SpiritualCreationsOils.com

Health and Resource Information

Eldercare Resources

www.101ElderCare.com/elder_care_resources

www.SeniorPlanningInc.com/

www.AgingCare.com/

*www.TheSeniorSource.org/pages/***eldercare***.html*

Care.com *(senior care resources* in your state)

Find financial planning and management, legal, home care, healthcare, end-of-life care, and housing options.

www.Care.com --› Senior Care --› Articles and Resources

Eldercare Resources

ELDERCARE RESOURCES is a geriatric care management company that offers a comprehensive array of elder care services for individuals and families.

www.eldercareResources.biz

Eldercare Resource Services
www.eldercareresourceservices.com/

Alternative Healing Clinics

The Hippocrates Health Institute
This is a good source for anyone who has serious health issues.

www.HippocratesHealthInstitute.com

Dr. Johanna Budwig
Dr. Budwig was one of Germany's top biochemists as well one of the best cancer researchers throughout all of Europe.

This is a great website with wonderful information for cancer and healing. There are some great recipes as well.

www.BudwigCenter.com/

Dr. Lorraine Day
Dr. Day discusses alternative therapy.

www.DrDay.com/

Gerson Institute
A non-profit organization in San Diego, California, dedicated to providing education and alternative treatments for cancer and other diseases.

www.Gerson.org

Water Purifiers

Nourishing Water - Life Ionizers

This company has whole-house water systems or filtration systems for the sink or shower.

www.LifeIonizer.com/nourishingwater/nourishingwater/

Groups and Various Health Information

Food and Water

This group can provide information on food and water, leading campaigns against toxic and unsafe food and water practices, and helping protect our water.

389 Rt. 215
Walden, VT 05873
(800) EAT–SAFE
www.FoodAndWater.org

The Cornucopia Institute

Seeking economic justice for the family-scale farming community.

www.Cornucopia.org/

Physicians Committee for Responsible Medicine

This is an amazing source of information on promoting preventative medicine, higher standards of ethics, and effective research.

5100 Wisconsin Ave. NW
Suite 404
Washington, DC 20016
(202) 686–2210
www.pcrm.org

Dr. Joseph Mercola

Dr. Mercola writes on various subjects concerning health and nutrition. He also sells many supplements, body products, etc. online. His newsletters are free, and he uses great resources for his information.

www.Mercola.com/

Health Counselor School

The Institute of Integrative Nutrition

Nancy went to this school and loved it! If you choose to enroll, tell them you heard about the school from Nancy!

www.IntegrativeNutrition.com/iinbook?erefer
=0015000000IyQPEAA3

Cooking Schools

The Natural Gourmet Institute for Food & Health

This school, located in New York City, provides two-hour classes, two weeks of classes, or entire chef training classes. They sell books, food, and supplies.

NaturalGourmetInstitute.com/

Alissa Cohen

Alissa teaches and certifies people in raw and living foods. Nancy is a certified raw food chef by Alissa.

www.AlissaCohen.com/

Kitchen Supplies

Williams-Sonoma

This store has a good selection of high-quality kitchen tools and equipment.

www.Williams-Sonoma.com/

Sur la Table

This store has a good selection of high-quality kitchen tools and equipment.

www.SurLaTable.com

Real Goods

Recycled and PBA-free containers. Good source for plastic bowls.

www.RealGoods.com/

Endnotes

1   Campbell-Falck, *Am J Emerg Med* 200: 18(1) 108: 111; and Pummer, "Influence of Coconut Water on Hemostasis," *Am J Emerg Med* 2001: 19(4); 287-289.

2   http://www.womenshealthmag.com/nutrition/cinnamon-benefits-explained

3   "ABUSED and Berated for Years...Now the New Nutritional Hero?"/"The 5 second 'Super Spray' 85% of People Need," Dr. Joseph Mercola's website, February 11, 2011, products.mercola.com/vitamin-d-spray/?source=nl.

4   Dr. Mary Newport, July 22, 2008, in her book *Alzheimer's Disease: What If There Was A Cure? The Story of Ketones,* Basic Health Publications, October 7, 2011. Dr. Newport's website offers free articles and recipes.

5   Paul Pitchford, *Healing with Whole Foods: Asian Traditions and Modern Nutrition, Third Edition.* North Atlantic Books, September 2002, p. 617.

6   "Goji Berries: Health Benefits and Side Effects,"
     WebMD website, June 29, 2011, www.webmd.
     com/balance/gogi=berries-health-benefits-
     and-side-effects.

7   Pitchford, *Healing with Whole Foods*, p. 619.

8   Ibid., p. 620.

9   Ibid.

10   Ibid., p. 621.

11   Ibid.

12   Ibid., p. 622.

13   "Dried Plums: More Than Just a Laxative,"
     Berkeley Newsletter, University of Califor-
     nia, September 3, 2010, www.berkeleywell-
     nessalerts.com/alerts/healthy_eating/Dried-
     Plums-Health-Benefits175-1.html.

14   Graedon, Joe and Teresa, "Pomegranates
     Have Many Health Benefits," *The Chon,
     Houston Lifestyle & Features, People's Phar-
     macy*, November 7, 2005, www.chron.com/
     life/article/Pharmacy=Pomgrantes-have-
     many-health-benefits-1950252.php.

15   Ibid.

16   Pitchford, *Healing with Whole Foods*, p. 624.

17 Mercola, Dr. Joseph, "Magnesium Can Reduce Your Risk of Sudden Death," Dr. Mercola's website, February 10 2011, articles.mercola.com/sites/articles/archive/2011/02/10/magnesium-can-reduce-your-risk-of-sudden-death.aspx.

18 Hendel, Barbara, and Peter Ferriera, "Water and Salt: The Essence of Life - The Healing Power of Nature," Natural Resources, January 1, 2003.

19 "Reduction in Blood Pressure with a Low Sodium, High Potassium, High Magnesium Salt in Older Subjects with Mild to Moderate Hypertension," *British Medical Journal* 301: 436–40, www.bmj.com/content/309/6952/436.

20 Christian Opitz, www.organiclivingfood.com/Products/CrystalBathSalt.html.

21 Staciokas, Linden, "Growing Sprouts Is Easy, Nutritious Way to Satisfy Veggie Cravings," *Fairbanks Daily News-Miner*, April 20, 2010, www.newsminer.com/view/full_story/7148528/article-Growing-sprouts-is-easy--nutritious-way-to-satisfy-veggie-cravings-.

22 "Not Such Sweet News about Agave," Berkeley Wellness Alert, December 17, 2010, www.berkeleywellnessalerts.com/alerts/healthy_eating/Agave-Versus-Refined-Sugar211-1.html.

23 "ABUSED and Berated for Years," Dr. Mercola's article on his website, February 24, 2011-issue 1667.

24 Mercola, Dr. Joseph, "Why the New Vitamin D Recommendations Spell Disaster for Your Health," Dr. Mercola's website, December 11 2010, articles.mercola.com/sites/articles/archive/2010/12/11/vitamin-d-update-carole-baggerly-and-dr-cannell.aspx.

25 Vanlint, Dr. Simon, "Indigenous People at Risk of Bone, Muscle Pain," Media Release, University of Adelaide (Australia), February 6, 2011, www.adelaide.edu.au/news/print43122.html.

26 Ibid.

27 May Bethel, The Healing Power of Natural Foods

28 Dr. Joseph Mercola, "Here's the Smarter Oil Alternative I Recommend to Replace Those Other Oils in Your Kitchen," Dr. Mercola's

website, mercola.com/products.mercola/com/coconut-oil/.

29 The web address is bodyecology.com/.

30 The recipes in this section are from Nancy's book *How to Be a Healthy Vegetarian*, pp. 153–157.

31 Dr. Bernard Jensen, *Nature Has a Remedy* (Escondido, Calif. : Self-published, 1979).

32 P. Airola, *How to Get Well* (Phoenix, Ariz.: Health Plus Publishers, 1984), p. 72.

This is one of my (Maryann's) father's favorite quotes.

"You can never
do a kindness
too soon
because,
You never know
How soon
It will be
Too late."
- Emerson

Acknowledgments

Maryann

My deepest thanks to my mother and to my father.

My mother has cooked every day for over 60 years. She never told us she didn't feel like cooking; she did it with love and devotion, and she is the best cook in the world. Thank you, Mom, for everything.

My deepest thanks to my father. He worked his entire life to give us a wonderful life. Thank you, Dad.

Mothers and fathers are the heroes of every child's story, and my parents are of mine. My love and thanks to my father and to my mother continues to flower.

Thank you to my sisters and brothers, Diane, Dominic, Dorothea, David, and Danny. You have helped with the cookbook more than you know.

Your dedication to our parents is love in action.

Thank you Carolyn King Bogart De Leo, Linda'Lee Colavito De Leo, and Joanna Weiss, my three sisters-in-law, for your love and support in everything I do. My father said it best: You became his daughters when you married my brothers, and you are my sisters.

To all my nieces and nephews: Michael, Jeremy, Christopher, Ethan, Lena, Dante, Lara, Dean, Kristyn, Jenni, Ava, and Jesse. Thank you for being part of my life. All of you enrich my life every day.

Thank you to my cousin Leeann Lavin. You inspire me with your zest for life. Thank you for writing a beautiful foreword.

Thank you, cousin Roni. Your kindness and love and support for me these past few years have been a godsend.

Thank you, Christine Koenig, Dai Sil Kim Gibson, Ellen Hilburg, Dr. Eileen Kenny, Juliette Hoffman, Angie Kenny, Monica Melamid, Helen Roche, Marcus Connaughton, Jan and Niel DeMarino, Isabel Vega and Vibha Bakshi, Susan Merz Anderson, Wayne Soben, and Terence Keating, Elizabeth Richter, Maria Lino, Kathy and Marianne Desmarais, and Jeannine and Denise Doyle. Your friendship, love, and support have been a blessing to me.

Thank you to all the chefs whose recipes I have used and pored over. I was inspired by so many: Giada De Laurentiis, Ina Garten, Marcella Hazan, Martha Stewart, Maryann Esposito, Lidia Bastianich, Jacques Pepin, Nigella Lawson, Michael Chiarello, and many more. There were many afternoons when I got inspiration from watching one of you on TV, and then went to my mother's kitchen and cooked something you made for my father.

Thank you to my grandmothers, Antoinette Buongiorno De Leo and Violet Colwell Terranova, and my grandfathers, Santo De Leo and George Terranova. They taught me to enjoy life. My Grandmother De Leo's one important rule about cooking has stayed with me: "Cook with the best quality ingredients you can find; that is what makes the best dish."

To all my aunts, uncles, cousins: Aunt Veronica, Aunt Loretta, Aunt Lorraine, Aunt Anna, Aunt Phyllis, Aunt Judy, Uncle Terry, Uncle Bobby, Uncle Carmine, Uncle Jerry, Uncle Frankie, Uncle Angelo, Aunt Roni, Uncle Jackie, Uncle Bill, cousins Christine, Laura, Roni and George, Marie, Jackie, Mary Ellen, Patty, Peter, Bill and Nancy, Jenny, Christopher, Bruce, Steven, Scott, Ross, Dolores, Toni, Joyce, Francis, Janet and Jimmy, Andrew and Lauren. I had a rich childhood because all of you were in it.

Thank you, Vimala Rodgers, for cheering me on always.

Thank you, Luanne Pennesi, RN, MS, practicing for over 30 years in both conventional and integrative medicine. Your laughter, love, and support paved the way for all of us to help my father through his illness. You are an inspiration to me and my family.

Thank you, Jodi Brandon, our brilliant editor, and Donna Kozik, for guiding us through the process of making the cookbook a reality.

Thank you Mariangela and Rita, Jason, Sergio and Jennifer, and all the lovely young people at Tarallucci E Vino. You brightened my mornings, and gave me a quiet place to write.

Thank you to all of Nancy's family, especially her dear and loving mother. I'm so happy that you have put some of your treasured family recipes into the book.

Thank you, Gene Aleinikoff and Ann Gordon for your support and help over the years. I'm blessed to have both of you as friends.

And to Nancy, my dear friend and co-author. You have put your heart and soul into our book with grace and love. You've been so generous to me, opening your home and your big Texas heart. It's meant so much to me to write this cookbook with you. I couldn't have done it without you. You've been a fun and faithful friend. Thank you.

Thank you, God, for my beautiful life; my wonder and awe at life never stops.

Nancy

First and foremost, I thank God for this gift. I am truly blessed to be a part of this book. May God bless this book and everyone who reads it.

I thank the following people:

Amanda and Gibbons

My two dear children have believed in me through our life's journey. Words cannot even begin to express the love and gratitude I feel for you two. You have encouraged me with undying support, inexhaustible faith, and constant love. You have been my biggest fans all of your lives, and I am so blessed to be able to call myself your mother. I love you!

My mother and family

I am grateful for your consistent and unwavering love through good and hard times. I am truly blessed to be a part of this family.

A special thank you to everyone who contributed recipes for this book: my mother, my children, Claire and Stefan, family friends, and many of my relatives who have passed on to be with God. Please accept my heartfelt thanks.

Maryann

I wish to thank my amazing friend and business partner, Maryann. I am so grateful that you asked me to write this book with you. It has been an incredible journey and experience. I thank God every day that we met. You have been there with me through some of the toughest times in my life, and you have always been there to cheer me on and be one of the dearest friends I could ever have wished for. Please accept my most heartfelt thanks.

Maryann's mother and family

Thank you all for the loving help, great recipes, and encouragement in this endeavor. It has been wonderful getting to know all of you better.

Paige Flink, Julianne Parker, Meredith Wagner,

Sandy Gaylord, and Michael Bolton, thank you so much for your part in bringing Maryann and me together. It has been an interesting and challenging journey, but your kindness, love, encouragement, and friendship have been invaluable. Deep and sincere thanks.

Thank you to my dear friends Dr. Gary Massad, Dr. Michael and Dr. Cara L. Hall, Linda Gray, Dr. Jan Goss, Eve Baughman Jung, TimWallace, Troy McNabb III, Susan and Joe Doyle, Elizabeth Marie, Deanna Sweet, Valerie Jarvis, Marsha Paisley, Carole Friezen, Stephanie Askew, Kimberly Wechsler, Tom Spicer, Mark Pharo, Karis Adam, Trish Aldredge, Suann and Ralph Davis, Anna Armstrong, Tom Fagadau, Lori Markman, Cynthia and Chip Jones, Kelley Willis, Candace Stone, Jeff Johnson, Christopher Koustoubardis, Carolyn Kalteyer, Judd Walker, Harrison Evans, Debbie Eulich Bell, Ann Lawther O'Dwyer, Julie Goss, Carol Brown, Prudie and Rick Koeninger, Priscilla Miller, Becky Crowe Nolan, John Luna, and the Queralt family for all of your help, generosity, and faith in me. I will always be grateful. Bless you.

A special thank you to all of my friends from Allie Beth Allman & Associates, who have been so supportive and cheered me on my journey.

A special thank you to all my dear clients. I have loved working with you.

Thank you Institute of Integrative Nutrition and all my friends that I met there. You have become some of my dearest friends. I have loved the journey with you.

Thank you to all my dear friends with the National Speakers Association: Adele Good, Kurt Boxdorfer, Dave Leiber, Bette Price, Tim Durkin, Stu Schlackman, Candace Fitzpatrick, Karen Cortell Reisman, Andrew Szabo, and Wendy Darling. I am so grateful for all of your help, encouragement, and friendship.

Thank you to all my friends from Highland Park. I appreciate you so very much.

Thank you to Eugene N. Aleinkoff for being so helpful and generous with your time and effort that you gave to Maryann and me when we were starting this project. I am very grateful and thankful for you kindness and continued support. Bless you.

Thank you, Lisa Endicott and all of your staff for your kindness, encouragement, and generosity.

To all of the wonderful friends and neighbors

from my life that have honored me with their friendship, never-ending patience, cheerful words of encouragement, and constant support, I thank you all for making my life so much richer and brighter. Bless you all.

Special thanks to our patient, caring, and wonderful editor, Jodi Brandon.

Special thanks to our publisher, Donna Kozik, her assistant, Deanna McAdams, and the staff, whose constant support and encouragement helped us to make this marvelous journey.

Thank you to Janice Olsen for our cover design.

Stevia
Cocunut oil
Chia seeds
Cucumber
parsely
Zucchini

6394720R00245

Made in the USA
San Bernardino, CA
08 December 2013